INTRODUCTION TO
MYCOLOGY

INTRODUCTION TO MYCOLOGY

Dr. Chelin Rani Gnanam

Former, Reader and Head
Department of Botany

Holy Cross College, Trichy

MJP PUBLISHERS

CHENNAI   NEW DELHI   TIRUNELVELI

ISBN 978-81-8094-198-6

MJP PUBLISHERS

New No. 5, Muthu Kalathy Street
Triplicane
Chennai 600 005

MJP 175   © Publishers, 2013

Publisher : J.C. Pillai

This book has been published in good faith that the work of the author is original. All efforts have been taken to make the material error-free. However, the author and publisher disclaim responsibility for any inadvertent errors.

To
My Lovely Daughter
R. SreeNirupa Singh

PREFACE

The present book Introduction to Mycology is an attempt to provide the basic, concise and indepth information about the various aspects of Fungi. The study of Fungi refreshes my mind which motivated me to write a book. There is an enormous increase in our knowledge of this group of biologically fascinating organisms. A general account of all major divisions of fungi proposed by Ainsworth (1973), the detailed life history of many genera are given to suit the needs and syllabi of Indian Universities. Classification of Fungi and Economic importance of Fungi are discussed in detail.

Many good books of foreign origin are available in India but these books are not within the reach of Indian students. The reasons are either they are not available in large numbers for the students or these are beyond the capacity of the students to get.

The book is not intended as a reference book for faculty members and research scholars since it does not provide an exhaustive account of Fungi. However, it is aimed to introduce the foundation of these interesting groups of living organisms which are intermediate between plants and animals.

With a long teaching experience, I have made an attempt to provide a complete information on fungi in this text. The language of the text is simple, vivid and the subject matter is provided with labeled illustrations for this text.

I do not claim this as my original research work. It is merely a compilation of information drawn from different research works. With the help of standard books of Indian an foreign authors, journals, research and review papers, the knowledge has been updated in this present text.

I thank the researchers, authors of books, publishers and editors whose publications have helped me in making out this text.

I would like to express my gratitude to my beloved teachers, Miss. Janaki Krishnan (Sarah Tucker College, Palayamkottai) and Mrs. Muthuvadivoo (Holy Cross College, Tiruchirapalli). The author gratefully acknowledges the help and encouragement given by Rev. Sr. Dona, Rev. Sr. Elizabeth Rose, Rev. Sr. Geraldine, Rev. Sr. Rosy and Rev. Sr. Annie Xavier the principals of Holy Cross College who motivated me at different stages and have been a source of inspiration.

I must thank Mr. Nandagopal, Reader in Botany (National College) who helped me in all possible ways.

With great pleasure. I express my profound appreciation to my husband Mr. Rajendrasingh, an advocate, daughter Er. Preeta singh and grand daughter Vaishnavi for their patience, support and constant co-operation during the entire period of preparation and publication of this book.

I express my heartfelt thanks to MJP Publishers, Mr. Janardhanan for the interest shown in bringing the book.

I sincerely invite constructive comments and valuable suggestions from the learned teachers and mycologists to further improve the book in subsequent editions.

Dr. Chelin Rani Gnanam

CONTENTS

1

INTRODUCTION

HISTORY OF MYCOLOGY

The Mycenean civilization, one of the greatest civilizations ever developed, may have been named after a legendary mushroom. According to the legend, the Greek hero Persius was thirsty and he by chance took up a mushroom (mykes) and he drank that water flowing from it and being pleased gave the place the name of Mycenae.

Derived from the Greek word, Mycology (Gr. *mykes* = mushroom + *logos* = discourse). etymologically, is the study of mushrooms. That is how mycology began in the dimpast for the mushrooms are among the largest fungi and attracted the attention of the naturalist before microscope or even simple lenses had been thought of. Fungus (pl.fungi) is a latin word which means mushroom. Mycology deals with life histories, relationship and evolutionary tendencies of fungi.

With the invention of the microscope by Anton van Leeuwenhoek in the 17th century, the systematic study of fungi began and the man who deserves the honour of being called the founder of the science of mycology is Antonio Micheli, the Italian botanist who in 1729, published Nova Plantarum Genera,which included his researches on fungi. Later Linnaeus (1753) in his book called Species Plantarum included fungi under Cryptogams and called them Cryptogamic fungi. Saccardo gave a detailed account of the structure and life histories of fungi in his book, *Sylloge Fungorum*.

In India, work on fungi was started by Butler in 1905. He was called the Father of Mycology in India. In 1931, Butler and Bishy wrote a book entitled " Fungi of India with a comprehensive account of fungi found in India".

Fungi are certainly not plants. They have amply sufficient distinctive features to set them well apart from both plants and animals and most would now accept that they merit a kingdom of their own. Unlike plants they cannot synthesize organic materials from carbon dioxide, mineral ions and water. Unlike animals they cannot ingest solids.

What are fungi? To define the exact limits of the group is very difficult. Traditionally, biologists have defined fungi, as eukaryotic spore-producing achlorophyllous organisms with absorptive nutrition which generally reproduce both sexually and asexually and are usually filamentous, branched somatic structures known as hyphae (sing. hypha), typically, are surrounded by cell walls. This is perhaps a good definition but it is not water tight. It's cell wall is made up of cellulose and chitin and the major reserve food is glycogen. They differ from other groups of plants in being heterotrophic and they are in fact described as chemoheterotrophs since they make use of readymade food materials from either living organisms or dead tissues. Whittaker (1969) raised fungi to the status of an independent kingdom in his Five kingdom concept due to their heterotrophic absorptive mode of nutrition.

HABITAT

Fungi grow in diverse habitats. They can grow in a wide range of natural habitats. They are found in every available habitat on earth where organic material (living or dead) is present. Fungi are universal in their distribution. They are almost present in the air we breathe, the water we drink and the food we eat. Majority of them prefer to grow in darkness and dim light in moist habitats.

Ecology of fungi has many attractive features. Based on their ecological habitat, fungi are classified into the following types:

1. Aquatic fungi
2. Soil fungi
3. Root-inhabiting fungi
4. Coprophilous fungi
5. Lignicolous fungi
6. Cellulolytic fungi
7. Keratinophilic fungi
8. Entomogenous fungi
9. Predacious fungi
10. Phylloplane fungi
11. Psychrophilic fungi
12. Thermophilic fungi
13. Ambrosia fungi

Aquatic Fungi

Only about 2% of the fungi are aquatic in that they normally complete their life cycle or at least the known part of it in water. Fungi were described from both freshwater and marine habitats. Fresh water fungi are found in freshwater lakes, rivers and streams. They are the Mastigomycotina which possess mobile zoospores, e.g., water moulds, mostly Saprolegniales and aquatic Hyphomycetes. Water moulds are common in wet soil. They occur on dead animal and plant remains such as seeds and fruits. They can be cultured by baiting techniques. They are either saprophytic or parasitic. A tiny sample of foam from a rapid well-aerated stream passing through woodland reveals many conidia which belong to aquatic Hyphomycetes. Aeroaquatic fungi are found on decaying leaves and twigs. Some members of Basidiomycotina and Ascomycotina are true marine fungi and they are mostly wood-inhabiting fungi.

Soil Fungi

Fungi which inhabit the soil are called soil fungi. They are mostly saprophytic and grow in soil rich in organic matter. Some facultative fungi are soil invaders. These are heterotrophic, which secrete extracellular enzymes that act upon the organic matter in the surrounding soil. These enzymes degrade the complex food substances into simpler substances which can pass through the fungal cell wall by simple diffusion.

Root-inhabiting Fungi

They are of two types, rhizosphere fungi and mycorrhizal fungi. The fungi that grow just in the vicinity of the root system are called rhizosphere fungi. They are helpful to roots in many ways such as absorption of nutrients and biological control of pathogens.

Mycorrhizal fungi are fungi that live in symbiotic association with the roots of higher plants such as gymnosperms and angiosperms. They are of three types.

i. *Ectomycorrhiza*   It is called sheathing mycorrhiza. The rootlets of the root system are completely covered by a distinct mantle or sheath of fungal hyphae from which the hyphae penetrate between the outermost cell layer or layers of the root. It is known as Hartignet. It absorbs water and nutrients from the soil and passes them on to the roots of the plant. In turn the fungi receive food and shelter. It enhances phosphate solubilization and absorption of phosphorus.

ii. *Endomycorrhiza*   There is no well-developed sheath. Most of the fungus is within the root and is intracellular. The fungus penetrates the cortical cells and forms fungal knots. Vesicular arbuscular mycorrhizal fungi (VAM fungi) produce vesicles and arbuscules in the cortex.

iii. *Ectendomycorrhiza*   It is intermediate between these two groups. The mycelium grow both intercellularly and intracellularly.

Coprophilous Fungi

Fungi that grow on dung or excretory matter of herbivorous animals (cow, goat, horse, etc.) are called coprophilous fungi. The excretory matter contains a specific substance called coprogen that induces the growth of these fungi, e.g., *Peziza* and *Pilobolus*. They can be cultured in the laboratory by using fresh dung incubated in a Petri dish.

Lignicolous Fungi

These are fungi which grow on wood or timber of higher plants. These fungi are able to use lignin, a secondary cell wall material, for their nutrition. They secrete lignolytic enzymes which are capable of degrading lignin, e.g., wood rotters or *Polyporus* sp. These species cause wood rotting and they produce large conspicuous fruit bodies or basidiocarps on the surface of woods. *Agaricus* spp. are able to decompose lignin on the straw of paddy and other cereals.

Cellulolytic Fungi

Fungi which grow on substrates rich in cellulose are called cellulolytic fungi. Cellulose is the primary cell wall material in plants. Some fungi like *Penicillium* and *Chaetomium* have the ability to degrade cellulose. They secrete cellulolytic enzymes which act upon cellulose and degrade it into glucose molecules. This can be used as a carbon source. *Penicillium* sp. growing on leather during rainy season is another example for cellulolytic fungi.

Keratinophilic Fungi

These are fungi which have the ability to degrade the hard keratin. They mainly grow on skin, nails and hairs and are called as dermatophytes. They cause ringworm, athletes feet and other related diseases, e.g., *Trichophyton, Epidermophyton* and *Microsporum.* They are able to spread form one host to another by physical contact between hosts. They have a saprophytic phase in soil. Dermatophytes can be isolated from soil by using degreased hair as a "bait".

Entomogenous Fungi

Fungi associated with insects and are parasitic on them are called entomogenous fungi. They attack all stages of insects—eggs, larvae, pupae and the adults. Members of Laboul beniales (Ascomycotina) which are obligate endoparasites of Coleoptera and Trichomycetes inhabit the digestive tract of many insects and arthropods. Entomophthorales (Zygomycotina) are parasitic on hemipteran and dipteran insects.

Predacious Fungi

Fungi which attack living nematodes and consume them are called predacious fungi, e.g., *Dactylaria* (Figure 1.1a), *Dactylella, Arthrobotrys robusta, Monacrosporium drechsleri.* These predatory fungi develop various types of trapping organs. The substance which induces trap formation is called nemin. The trapping organs are adhesive knobs, adhesive lateral branches, adhesive nets, non-constricting rings and constricting rings.

Adhesive knobs are single-celled, sessile or stalked, globose knobs, covered by a sticky substance (Figure 1.1 b). Adhesive lateral branches are short lateral branches composed of a few cells which are held in an upright position above the level of the mycelium. It is covered by a film of adhesive. Thus the nematodes become attached to the adhesive branches. Adhesive nets are networks formed by the anastomosing of the recurved branch tips of a lateral branch system. The surface of the trap is lined by an adhesive film (Figure 1.1c and e). Non-constricting rings are three-celled rings formed by recurved anastomosis of the tip of a lateral branch (Figure 1.1d). In the constricting rings, when the inner surface of the ring is stimulated by contact, the individual cells rapidly inflate and occlude the lumen of the trap thereby constricting a nematode it surrounds (Figure 1.1f). The fungus produces a haustorium which pierces the cuticle and body wall of the nematode. This forms an infection bulb from which many assimilative hyphae develop in both directions consuming the body contents (Figure 1.1e).

Figure 1.1 a–f. Trapping structures of some predacious Fungi-Imperfecti. a—*Dactylaria candida*. Conidiophores, conidia and stalked knob trap, b—*Monacrosporium drechsleri*. Hyphae with short lateral branches modified as adhesive knobs, c—*Arthrobotrys robusta*. Mycelium with anastomosing adhesive nets. d—*Dactylaria candida*. Non-constricting ring traps, e,f—constricting rings of *Arthrobotrys* and *Monacrosporium* respectively.

Phylloplane Fungi

These are fungi which are able to complete their life cycle on the living leaf without damaging it, e.g., *Sporobolomyces*, *Cladosporium* and *Aureobasidium*. *Cladosporium* sps. form extensive colonies in the phylloplane. The nutrient sources of phylloplane inhabitants may be organic substances absorbed or deposited onto leaves.

Psychrophilic Fungi

These are fungi which grow best at low temperatures, usually below 5°C. Some psychrophilic fungi are *Candida gelide*, *Sclerotinia boreatis* and *Typhula trifolii*. Both polar regions support these fungi. Species of *Fusarium*, *Sclerotinia* and *Typhula* are called snow moulds as they cause diseases of cereals, grasses and food crops grown at low temperatures. Many fungi occur in frozen foods. *Aureobasidium pullulans* is very common. Black spot of chilled or frozen meat is caused by *Cladosporium herbarum* that grows between 6°C and 0°C on infected meat.

Thermophilic Fungi

A thermophilic fungus is one whose minimum temperature for growth is 20°C or above and maximum temperature for growth is 50°C and above. They are called thermotolerant mesophiles. Common thermopilous fungi are *Aspergillus fumigatus, Penicillium emersonii, Mucor pusillus* and *Humicola insolens*. Beneficial activities of these fungi include preparation of mushroom compost, disposal of municipal waste and rotting of fibres. The detrimental effects include deterioration of stored cereal grains and self-heating, leading to spontaneous combustion of hay, peat, and wood chips.

Ambrosia Fungi

It lives in ecto-symbiotic association with the wood-boring beetles which introduce into their tunnels, the ambrosia fungi that grow and line the walls of the entire tunnel system and serve as the chief source of food for all stages of the beetle. The fungi are constantly associated with beetles and are transmitted by them frequently in specialized organs called mycetangia or mycangia. These are pouchlike structures which helps in the transportation of the fungus. This fungus is *Monilia candida*.

SOMATIC OR VEGETATIVE PHASE

Thallus and kinds of Mycelia

Some fungi are unicellular, e.g., yeast, but the majority have a differentiated thallus consisting of threadlike tubular filaments, the **hyphae** (Gr.hypha—web). The mass of hyphae constituting the thallus is called **mycelium**. In most fungi the thallus is differentiated into a vegetative part which absorbs nutrients and a reproductive part which forms reproductive structures. Such thalli are called **eucarpic**. In some, however, the thallus does not show this differentiation and after a phase of vegetative growth, changes into one or more reproductive structures. Such thalli are called **holocarpic**. The hyphae are branched or unbranched and the branches ramify on or inside the substratum to form a three-dimensional network. Hyphae grow entirely at their tips.

The mycelium may be septate or aseptate.

Aseptate mycelium In Phycomycetes the hyphae are aseptate and multinucleate and are called coenocytic mycelium (Figure 1.2). The mycelium grows terminally by the apical elongation of the hyphae accompanied by increase in the number of nuclei by nuclear divisions. Septae, however, are formed to cut off reproductive structures or to seal off a damaged portion.

Septate mycelium Members of Ascomycetes and Basidiomycetes develop internal cross walls called septae which divide the hyphae into segments (Figure 1.3). The septa appear at regular intervals behind the hyphal tips. The segments may be uninucleate or multinucleate and the septa are transverse. The formation of septum is always preceded by the division of nucleus.

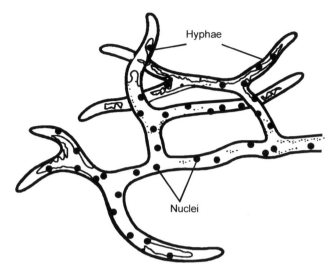

Figure 1.2 Fungi. Filamentous thallus. Aseptate coenocytic mycelium

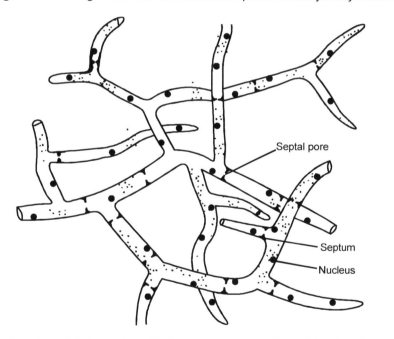

Figure 1.3 Fungi. Filamentous thallus. Septate mycelium with uninucleate cells

Fungi have eukaryotic cell structure. They have double-membrane-bound cell organelles like nucleus, mitochondria, tubular endoplasmic reticulum (ER), Golgi bodies and ribosomes. The presence of **lomasomes** which appear as vesicles between the cell wall and plasma membrane is an unusual feature.

Fungal cell wall contains 80–90% carbohydrates. A special feature of fungal cell wall is the presence of chitin and not cellulose. Cellulose occurs in the cell walls of Oomycetes and Hyphochytridiomycetes.

Types of Septa

The septa are divided into two types, primary and adventitious septa. Primary septa are seen in Ascomycetes and Basidiomycetes and are formed in association with nuclear division. Adventitious septa are found in Phycomycetes and are formed to delimit the reproductive structures like sporangia or gametangia.

Based on the morphology, four types of septa are recognized (Figure 1.4 a–d).

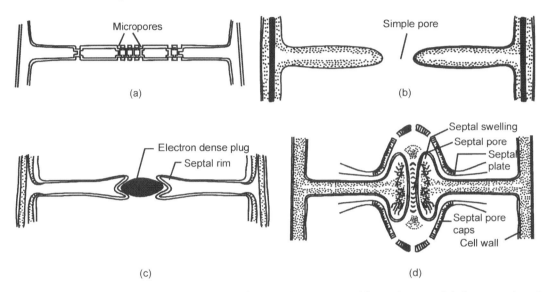

Figure 1.4   Diagrammatic representation of the various types of fungal septa. (a) Septum showing micropores (Geotrichum). (b) Septum with simple pores (most of the Ascomycetes and Deuteromycetes). (c) Septum of Trichomycetes. (d) Dolipore septum (most of the Basidiomycetes excepting rusts and smuts) (After Barnett. 1976).

1. *Solid septum*   It is a primitive type of septum. The septal wall is complete without any perforation or opening. It is formed to demarcate the sex organs or reproductive structures.

2. *Perforated septum*   Septum is perforated with one or more openings that permit movement of cytoplasm from one cell to another (Figure 1.4a).

3. *Ascomycetean septum*   There is a single perforation in the septum (Figure 1.4b).

4. *Bordered-pit type septum*   Septum resembles the bordered pit of angiosperms. It is seen in Trichomycetes. The septal rim is swollen and there is a central electron-dense plug of materials, which regulates the flow of cytoplasm from one cell to the other (Figure 1.4c).

5. *Dolipore septum*   In Basidiomycetes this septum is well developed and is a complicated type. The rim of the central pore is swollen and thickened to form a barrel-shaped structure with open ends which are guarded by caplike cover. This appears as a round bracket or parenthesis in sectional view. The septal pore cap is therefore called the parenthosome. It permits the movement of cytoplasm, mitochondria and nuclei from cell to cell. It is one of the identifying features of Basidiomycetes (Figure 1.4d).

Structures Associated with Somatic Mycelium

1. *Rhizoid*   They are small colourless threadlike branched or unbranched structures formed in the somatic mycelium. They penetrate the substratum on which the mycelium grows and are helpful in anchoring the thallus and in the absorption of food materials from the substratum, e.g., *Mucor* and *Rhizopus*.

2. *Appressoria*   The hyphae of many plant pathogenic fungi develop special structures for attachment to the host in the early stages of infection. They are localized swellings of the tips of germ tubes that develop in response to contact with the host. From these swollen tips, a minute infection peg usually grows and enters the epidermis of the host.

3. *Haustoria*   Many biotrophs and some facultative parasites possess haustoria which are lateral outgrowths of intercellular hyphae specially modified for absorption of nutrients. They are of various shapes and sizes ranging from knoblike structures to simple, lobed, branched, coiled or coralloid. Haustoria penetrate the cell wall but dot not rupture the plasma membrane.

4. *Hyphal traps*   Hyphal traps are found in predacious fungi for the capture of small animals, protozoa or nematodes. Hyphal traps are the modified hyphae. There are mainly two types of predacious activity, viz., capture by adhesion and capture by mechanical traps. The fungi which capture their prey by adhesion produce sticky substance on which the victims are held. Lateral adhesive branches are formed in Dactylella. In *Arthrobotrys oligospora*, an adhesive network is formed. It is formed by the anastomosis of short, curved, lateral branches with the neighbouring branches to form a complex network in which eelworms become entangled and are held by the sticky secretion produced by the cells of the loops. Mechanical traps are formed in *Dactylaria candida* and it consists of a ring of three cells borne on a lateral branch which swells to about three times its original volume on coming in contact with the prey.

Aggregation of mycelia

Fungal mycelium is a mass of hyphae interwoven loosely to form a network and the hyphae sometimes are altered in shape and undergo various modifications. Such a false tissue is called plectenchyma. It is of two types, prosenchyma and pseudoparenchyma.

Prosenchyma   It is rather a loosely woven tissue of hyphae. They run more or less parallel to one another and are composed of elongated cells (Figure 1.5a).

Pseudoparenchyma   When the hyphae become woven and intertwined into a compact mass, it is called pseudoparenchyma. The walls of the hyphae get fused and lose their identity. As a result, the hyphal mass appears to be a continuous structure consisting of isodiametric or oval cells. It resembles the parenchyma tissue of higher plants (Figure 1.5 b).

Plectenchymatous tissues in higher fungi are formed in somatic structures such as stromata, sclerotia and rhizomorphs (Figure 1.5 c–f). In general these structures are divisible into two anatomical regions, an outer hard ring called cortex made of pigmented pseudoparenchyma and the inner soft, hyaline, prosenchymatous core, called medulla.

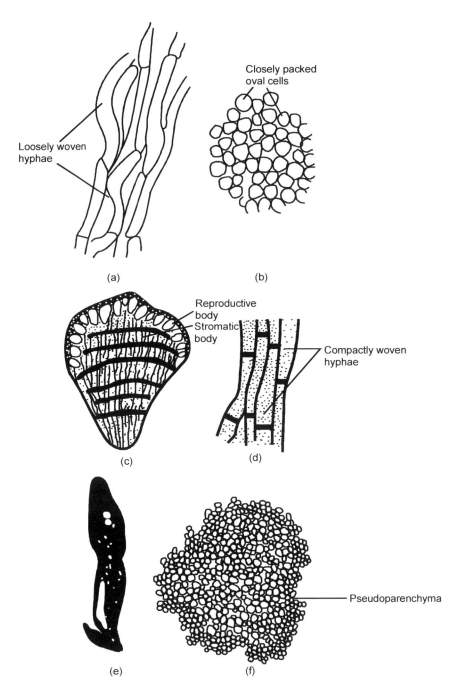

Figure 1.5 Hyphal modifications to form fungal tissues (a, b) and somatic structrues (c–f). (a) Prosenchyma. (b) Pseudoparenchyma. (c, d) Stroma of *Daldinia* (c) Section (d) Structural detail (e–f) Sclerotium of *Claviceps purpurea* (e) Sclerotium (f) Cross section.

FLAGELLATION IN FUNGI

The number, kind and position of flagella on motile cell constitutes flagellation. It plays an important role in the taxonomy of lower fungi or Phycomycetes. The higher fungi lack motile cells in the life cycle. The motile cells such as zoospores and gametes in the lower fungi are furnished with one or two fine protoplasmic whiplike threads known as flagella. They are thin hairlike emergences of the cell cytoplasm which function as locomotory structures. There is a single anterior or posterior flagellum or they occur as a pair in the cell (Figure 1.6 a–e).

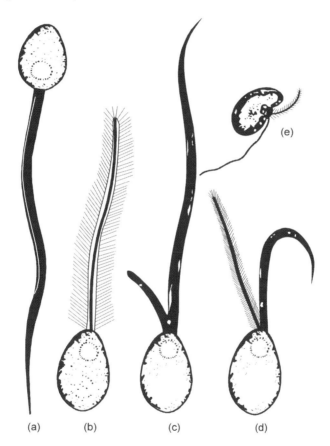

(a) (b) (c) (d)

Figure 1.6 (a–e) Flagellation in the lower fungi

Each flagellum has a central axial filament called axoneme which is surrounded by a cytoplasmic sheath. In C.S. the axoneme is composed of eleven fibrils (two central and nine peripheral). The nine peripheral fibrils are double in nature (Figure 1.7e).

Kinds of flagella   Three types of flagella are reported.

i.   **Whiplash type**   It is a smooth flexible type of flagellum which has a narrow end piece. The end piece is naked and is not surrounded by the cytoplasmic sheath (Figure 1.7a).

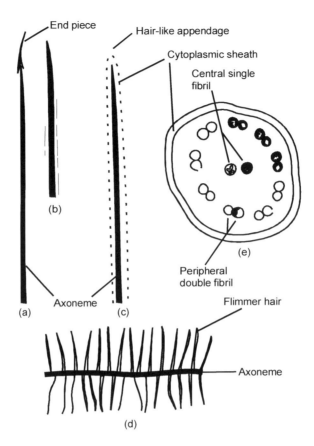

Figure 1.7   (a–e) Fungal flagella. a—L.S. of upper portion of an acronematic or whiplash flagellum with a drawn-out pointed tip or end piece. b—L.S. of whiplash flagellum with blunt tip. c—L.S. of Pantonematic or tinsel flagellum. d—Diagrammatic representation of a part of the tinsel flagellum from an electron micrograph (Based on Manton *et al.*). e—T.S. of eukaryotic flagellum showing 9 + 2 arrangement of fibrils

   ii.   Blunt type   It is like whiplash type of flagellum that has a smooth surface but it lacks the end piece (Figure 1.7b).

   iii.   Tinsel type   It is a heavy type of flagellum without end piece. It bears fine lateral hair-like appendages known as flimmer hairs on its surface (Figure 1.7c and d).

NUTRITION IN FUNGI

Method of nutrition in fungi is very specific and is different from other groups of plants. Fungi are heterotrophs which depend on external supply of readymade organic food which they get as parasites or saprophytes. Unlike animals, their nutrition is absorptive.

Fungi are described as chemotropic heterotrophs since they make use of the readily available nutrients from the surrounding medium. Fungal hyphae lie in direct contact with the nutrients and absorb dissolved smaller molecules such as simple sugars and amino acids. Large insoluble substances like polysaccharides, fats and proteins are first broken down into simpler compounds which can be absorbed. This is carried out by secreting extracellular enzymes which act upon the complex food materials in the surrounding medium.

These extracellular enzymes are produced within the hyphal cells and are included in special cytoplasmic vesicles. These vesicles move gradually into the plasma membrane and from the plasma membrane they reach the surrounding medium through the pores that are found in the cell wall. Only particles with molecular weight as small as 15,000 dalton can pass through the pores. The regulation of movement of the nutrients is achieved by permeases which can bind only to certain substances. There is a high degree of specificity of permeases.

Nutritional Requirements

Fungi, like other organisms, require all essential elements for growth. Fungi need about 17 elements, some in extremely small or trace amounts and called micro- or trace elements and others in comparatively large amounts, and therefore, called macro-elements.

The macro-elements include non-metallic elements (carbon, hydrogen, oxygen, nitrogen, sulphur and phosphorus) and metallic elements (potassium and magnesium). The metallic elements are functional elements active in metabolism and the non-metallic elements in general serve as structural elements. The essential micro-elements are iron, zinc, copper, manganese and molybdenum. The micro-elements act as cofactors or activators of enzymes and are also used in the synthesis of vitamins. These are essential for growth and sporulation.

Carbon source   Fungi depend on external supply of organic carbon compounds. About 50% of the dry weight of fungi is contributed by carbon compounds. Carbon serves as a source of energy and as the chief structural element. Cell wall material such as cellulose, chitin, hemicellulose and pectin are synthesized from carbon compounds. Simple sugars like glucose and fructose are used as carbon source. Some fungi use maltose as a source of carbon and maltose is formed by the degradation of starch. Cellulose is used as a source of carbon by cellulolytic fungi. These fungi produce many enzymes which break down cellulose into glucose, and such enzymes include exoglucanase, endoglucanase and β-glucosidase

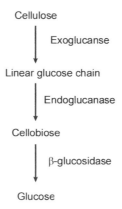

Hydrogen and oxygen   Hydrogen and oxygen are supplied in dissolved form in water which is the major constituent of fungal mycelium.

Nitrogen   Fungi use both organic and inorganic materials as a source of nitrogen. The chief organic sources are protein, peptide or amino acid. Many fungi utilize nitrates as the sole source of nitrogen. Some fungi use nitrites and ammonium salts. Some soil-inhabiting fungi like *Rhodotorula* and *Pullularia pullulans* fix atmospheric nitrogen. Fungi use organic nitrogen in the form of amino acids and amides.

Sulphur   Fungi derive their sulphur from sulphate ions.

Phosphorus   It is utilized as phosphate ions. Both organic and inorganic phosphate esters are utilized.

Fungi require complex organic compounds for growth and these are the vitamins or growth factors. Many fungi synthesize their own supply of vitamins and are called auxo-autotrophs which do not need exogenous supply of vitamins. There are others which depend on an external source, because they are unable to synthesize vitamins and are called auxotrophs. The important vitamins are thiamine, biotin, pyridoxine and riboflavin.

Mechanism of Nutrition

The entire mycelium may have the power to absorb nutrients or it may be carried out by specialized portions of the mycelium like **rhizoids** or **haustoria**. In saprophytic fungi the hyphae directly absorb smaller soluble molecules such as simple sugars and amino acids by direct diffusion. Insoluble complex substances are broken down into simpler substances and then absorbed.

In parasitic fungi the haustoria act as food-sucking organs. Haustorium is intracellular and it penetrates the host cell wall and reaches the cytoplasm from which it absorbs the food materials.

In parasitic fungi the mycelium is either intercellular or intracellular. The intercellular mycelium produces haustoria by which food materials are absorbed. The intracellular mycelium is already in direct contact with the host protoplasm and it obtains its food by direct diffusion.

Basic Concepts of Nutrition

- ⊙   In fungi, digestion of food materials occurs in the external environment with the help of extracellular enzymes secreted by the fungi into the surrounding medium.
- ⊙   The breakdown products of complex food materials are utilized not only by the fungi but also by other microorganisms. This is the reason for the profuse growth of microorganisms in the vicinity of fungi.
- ⊙   Moisture or water drops are needed for the growth of fungi. A water film is needed for diffusion of enzymes and nutrients and the activation of enzymes is carried out in the presence of water. This is the main reason for the luxuriant growth of fungi in moist environment.
- ⊙   Fungi can regulate the environment in which they grow. Some fungi can change the pH of the surrounding medium in which they grow. For example, *Sclerotinia* secretes large amount of oxalic acid into the surrounding medium that reduces the pH to 4 and the medium becomes acidic. At this pH, the enzymatic action is enhanced.

⊙ Fungi can create zones or areas of substrate exhaustion or enzymic erosion. These zones are seen just around the fungal mycelium. These represent the areas where the nutrients are completely exhausted by fungal mycelia. Once the nutrients are completely utilized, the mycelium invades new areas. This is the reason for the rapid growth of fungal mycelium.

REPRODUCTION IN FUNGI

Reproduction is the formation of progeny by either vegetative, asexual or sexual means.

Vegatative Reproduction

Vegetative reproduction in effected by fragmentation, fission, budding, arthrospores or oidia, chlamydospores, gemmae, sclerotia and rhizomorphs.

1. *Fragmentation* The fungal hyphae break into small pieces and each piece may later grow into a new mycelium.

2. *Fission* It is a common method of reproduction in fission yeasts. Here the cell divides into two daughter cells of identical size which separate by constriction or transverse walls. (Figure 1.8b).

3. *Budding* It is a common method in budding yeasts. A small outgrowth or bud emerges from the parent cell and the nucleus of the parent cell divides into two. One of the nuclei is incorporated into the bud and this may or may not be separated form the parent cell. When it is not separated from the parent cell, it produces another bud. Thus the process is repeated several times resulting in the formation of a chain of buds called a pseudo-mycelium (Figure 1.8a).

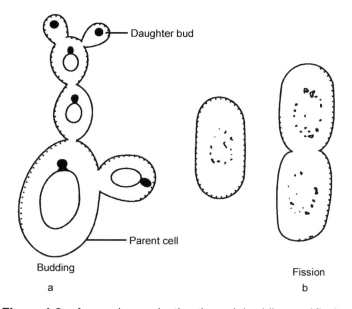

Budding
a

Fission
b

Figure 1.8 Asexual reproduction through budding and fission

4. *Arthrospores*   In some fungi specialized vegetative hypae divide by frequent septation into cylindrical spores called arthrospores or oidia (Figure 1.9a).

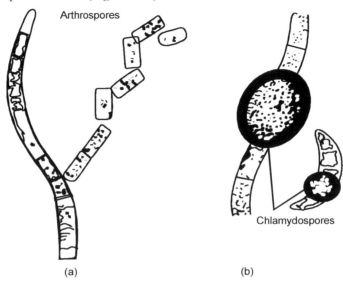

Figure 1.9 (a–b)   Asexual reproduction through spores. (a)—arthrospores; (b)—chlamydospores

5. *Chlamydospores*   Chlamydosores are thick-walled, resistant spores formed by terminal or intercalary cells of the hypha and are released after death of hyphae. In the formation of chlamydospores, the cells round off, usually enlarge and develop a thick-coloured wall. The cytoplasm becomes dense with enough reserve food. They are resistant to lysis by chemicals produced by other soil organisms. (Figure 1.9b).

6. *Gemma*   They resemble chlamydospores in structure but are not thick-walled. They occur singly or in chain and are borne terminally, e.g., Saprolegniales and *Mucor*.

7. *Sclerotia*   Sclerotia are rounded mass of hyphae and are resistant structures. They may remain dormant for long periods of time and germinate during favourable season. They do not have spores, e.g., *Claviceps purpurea* and *Polyporus mylittae*.

Asexual Reproduction

Asexual reproduction occurs under favourable conditions. It takes place by the formation of numerous spores which are uni- or multicellular and microscopic, and contain one or more nuclei which are liberated from the parent thallus passively or actively. Asexual spores are of two main types, sporangiospores and conidia.

1. *Sporangiospores*   These are asexual spores produced endogenously in reproductive structures called **sporangia**. They are produced in lower fungi and are of various sizes or shapes. The protoplast of the sporangium undergoes cleavage to form many **sporangiospores** and they escape through the exit papillae or a pore or by a discharge tube at the distal end or through an apical opening formed by a cap or lid. In the terrestrial fungi the spores are released by the rupture of the sporangial wall.

The released spores are motile in the aquatic forms and non-motile in terrestrial forms. The former are called **zoospores** and the latter are called **aplanospores** (Figure 1.10).

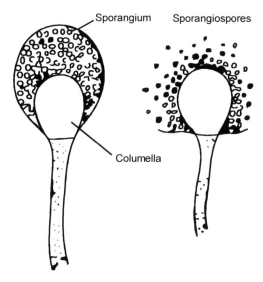

Figure 1.10   Sporangiospores

i. *Zoospores*   The zoospores may be uniflagellate (Chytridiomycetes and Hyphochytridiomycetes) or biflagellate (Plasmodiophoromycetes and Oomycetes). In Chytridionmycetes, the single flagellum is of whiplash type and is attached at the posterior end. In Hyphochtridiomycetes the single flagellum is of tinsel type and is attached at the anterior end. In Plasmodiophoromycetes, the biflagellate zoospores have two flagella at the anterior end and one flagellum is of whiplash type and the other is of blunt type. In Oomycetes, the zoospores are biflagellated and the flagella are attached at the anterior or lateral end, and one flagellum is of whiplash type and the other is of tinsel type (Figure 1.11).

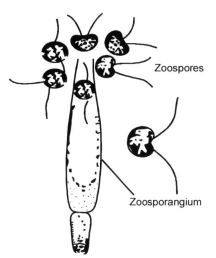

Figure 1.11   Zoospores

ii. *Aplanospores* In terrestrial fungi, asexual reproduction is by means of non-motile wind-disseminated spores known as the aplanospores. They are produced in sporangia which are borne on simple or branched sporangiophores. In *Mucor*, the large multispored columellate sporangia are borne singly and terminally on unbranched sporangiophores. In other forms of Mucorales, small sporangia or sporangiola with few spores or single-spored sporangia are produced.

2. *Conidia* Conidia are of two types—1.*Thallospores* (arthrospores and chlamydospores) and 2. *Conidiospores* or true conidia. Thallospores are formed by transformation of pre-existing cells of the thallus and are detached by decay of the hyphae or disarticulation of the cells. The conidiospores are formed as new structures on the thallus and are easily detachable.

Conidia are commonly produced in Ascomycotina and fungi imperfecti. In some lower fungi like *Albugo,* the sporangia in dry weather behave like conidia and germinate directly by putting forth a germ tube. In higher fungi, conidia are borne on conidiophores which may be free or aggregated to form compound sporophores like synnemata or sporodochia. In Deuteromycotina, the conidiophores are borne inside structures called fruiting bodies which may be saucer-shaped in acervuli or flask-shaped or globular in pycnidium.

In Ascomycotina, the conidiophore may be unbranched *(Aspergillus)* or branched *(Penicillium).* In *Aspergillus*, it bears a vesicle at its end and many small flask-shaped structures called phialides or sterigmata are borne on it. Sometimes the primary sterigma produces secondary and tertiary sterigmata. Conidia are formed at the tip of the sterigmata in basipetal chain. The tip of each phialide functions as a growing point and cuts the conidia (Figure 1.12).

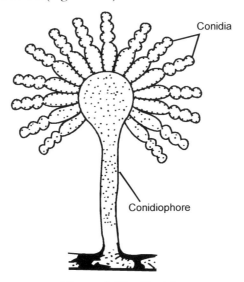

Conidia

Conidiophore

Figure 1.12 Conidia

Sexual Reproduction

Sexual reproduction involves three different phases—plasmogamy, karyogamy and meiosis—occurring in a cyclic manner. Plasmogamy is the fusion of two protoplasts of two gametes. Karyogamy involves the fusion of two nuclei to form a diploid zygote nucleus and meiosis is the formation of four haploid spores by the process of nuclear division.

The sexual cycle of different fungi may vary due to variation in timings of the above events. In Ascomycotina and Basidiomycotina, plasmogamy and karyogamy are separated in space and time. The compatible nuclei do not undergo karyogamy immediately after plasmogamy but remain paired to form a dikaryon. The dikaryon persists for a varying time and undergoes conjugate division. A new phase called dikaryotic phase is introduced in the life cycle.

In Deuteromycotina, the phenomenon of parasexuality is seen in which plasmogamy, karyogamy and haploidization occur in a definite sequence but not at the specified points in the life cycle.

There are seven methods by which the compatible nuclei are brought together. These modes are often referred to as methods of sexual reproduction. These are as follows:

- Planogametic copulation
- Gametangial contact
- Hologamy
- Autogamy
- Gametangial copulation
- Spermatization
- Somatogamy

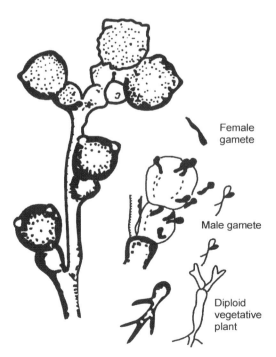

Figure 1.13   Planogametic copulation (*Allomyces arbuscula*).

1. ***Planogametic copulation***   This involves fusion of two naked, free gametes, one or both of which may be motile. The motile gametes are called planogametes. Depending on the size and motility of fusing gametes, there are three types of planogametic copulation—isogamy, anisogamy and oogamy. When the two fusing gametes are of the same size and shape, they are called isogametes, e.g., Chytridiales. In anisogamy the two planogametes are morphologically similar but different in size, e.g., Blastocladiales (*Allomyces*) (Figure 1.13). In oogamy there is fusion of a motile male gamete with a non-motile female gamete (oosphere) contained in an oogonium, e.g., Monoblepharidales. The motile male gamete or antherozoid enters the oogonium and fertilizes the egg or oosphere [Figure 1.14(a–e)].

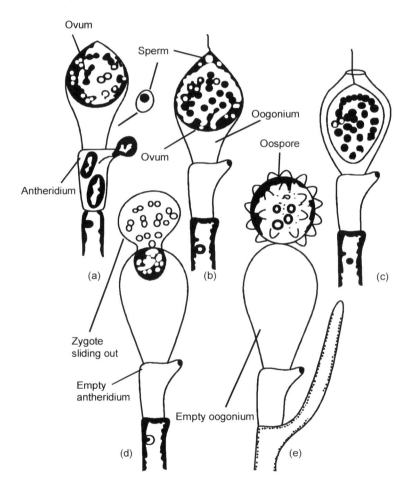

Figure1.14 (a–e). Lower fungi. Oogamous sexual reproduction in *Monoblepharis*. Plasmogamy by ooplanogametic copulation (After Laibach).

2. ***Gametangial contact***   It is seen in Oomycetes and some Ascomycetes. There is morphological differentiation of sex organs such as male and female sex organs. The male gametangium is called the antheridium and the female gametangium is called the oogonium. The oogonium may contain one or many eggs. At the time of sexual act, the antheridium and oogonium come in contact and they do not

actually fuse. The antheridium puts forth a slender tubular outgrowth at the point of contact with the oogonium and this known as the fertilization tube. It pierces the oogonial wall and releases the male nucleus into the oogonium where it fuses with the female nucleus thereby bringing about fertilization. In Saprolegniales, the oogonium produces many eggs and is fertilized by more than one antheridia. Many fertilization tubes are formed around the oogonium. (Figure 1.15 (a–f)). In other Oomycetes, the oogonium produces a single egg in the ooplasm that is surrounded by periplasm (Figure 1.16 a–n). In Ascomycetes, the female sex organ is called the ascogonium containing one to many nuclei. The male sex organ is called the antheridium. The ascogonium may or may not have a trichogyne.

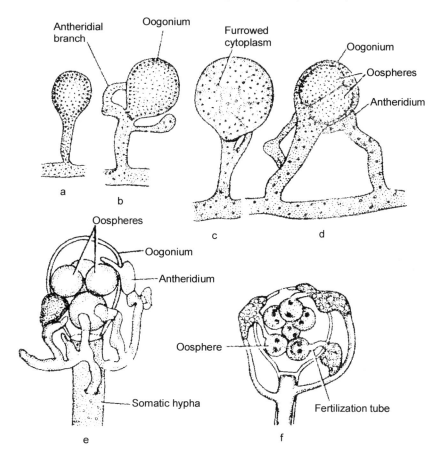

Figure 1.15 (a–f) *Saprolegnia litoralis*, (a–d)—Development of oogonium (note the young antheridial branch in b, furrowed cytoplasm of oogonium in c, and formation of zoospores in d); e—terminal oogonium with antheridia; f—separate fertilization tube for different oospheres

Gametangial contact takes place between the ascogonium and antheridium. One nucleus from the antheridium reaches the ascogonium and forms a pair with the fertile ascogonial nucleus. This pair of nuclei is called a dikaryon (Figure 1.17 a–c).

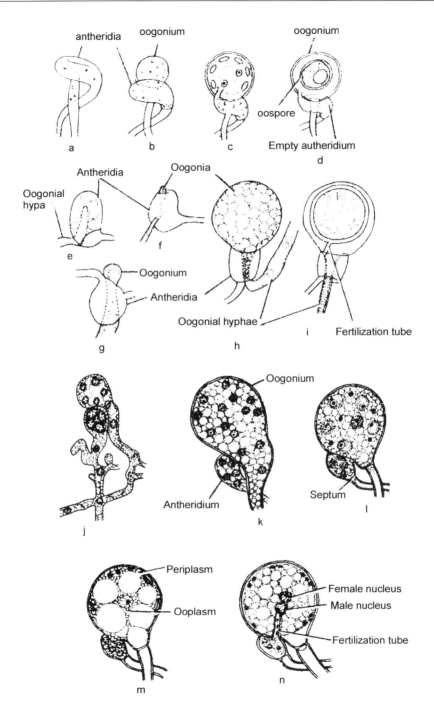

Figure 1.16 (a–n) Sexual reproduction in *Phytophthora*. (a–d)—in *P.infestans*; (e–i)—in *P. erythroseptica*; (j–n)—in *P. cactorum* [(a – d) modified after Smooth et al; (e–i)— modified after Webster; j–n, modified after Blackwell]

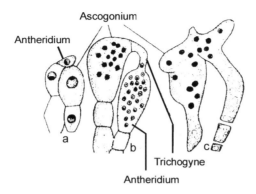

Figure 1.17 (a–c)   Ascomycetes. Diagram illustrating plasmogamy by gametangial contact. a—uninucleate sex organs of *Sphaerotheca*, ascogonium lacks trichogyne; b—multinucleate sex organs of *Pyronema*, ascogonium furnished with a trichogyne; c—multinucleate sex organ of *Claviceps*, ascogonium without trichogyne

3. *Hologamy*   It is a type of gametangial copulation in which fusion takes place between two mature somatic cells functioning as gametangia. No gametes are formed in this case, e.g., Yeasts. The gametangia fuse in pairs. The resultant fusion cell has a diploid nucleus (Figure 1.18 a–d).

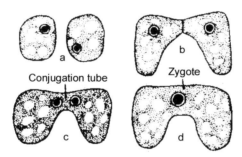

Figure 1.18 (a–d)   Ascomycetes. Stages illustrating hologamy in *Schizosaccharomyces octosporus*. a—two haploid mature somatic cells which function as gametangia; b—each gametangium putting out a protuberance; c—the two protuberances unite with each other to form a conjugation tube; d—The two sexual nuclei fuse in the conjugation tube

4. *Autogamy*   In *Talaromyces vermiculatus* syn. *Penicillium vermiculatum*, the antheridia are either absent or when formed they are non-functional. The female sex organ is called the ascogonium and the male sex organ is the antheridium which is produced at the tip of the antheridial branch. When the antheridium touches the ascogonium, there is dissolution of the walls at the point of contact. There is no migration of male protoplast or nucleus into the ascogonium. Mere contact stimulates the ascogonial nuclei to arrange themselves in functional pairs or dikaryons. Though the antheridium is produced morphologically, it is non-functional. Thus this method of sexual reproduction is called autogamy (Figure 1.19 a–b).

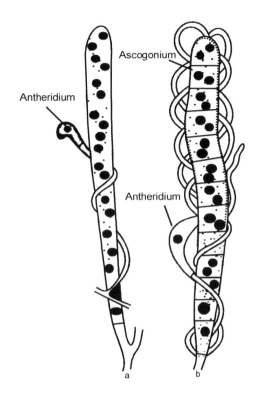

Figure 1.19 (a–b) Ascomycetes. Stages illustrating autogamy in *Talaromyces vermiculatus* (*Penicillium vermiculatum*) (After Dangeard, 1907)

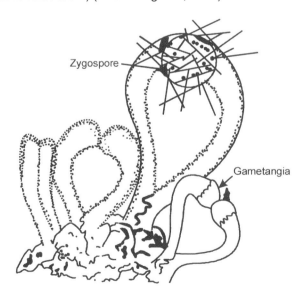

Figure 1.20 Gametangial copulation (*Phycomyces blakesleeanus*)

5. *Gametangial copulation*   The entire contents of the two gametangia fuse and become one. The uniting gametangia are morphologiclly similar (isogamous) or they are dissimilar or unequal in size (anisogamous). Isogametangial copulation is seen in *Rhizopus* and *Mucor*. When two hyphae of opposite strains come in contact, each produces a short lateral copulating branch, the progametangium. The tips of progametangia enlarge and divide thus forming a terminal gametangium and a basal suspensor. During sexual fusion the intervening walls between the two gametangia dissolve forming a fusion cell. There is mingling of the protoplasts of the two gametangia. The nuclei of opposite strains fuse to form diploid nuclei. The young zygospore secretes a wall around it and forms a thick dark sculptured thickening around the zygospore (Figure 1.20).

In *Zygorhynchus*, there is anisogamous copulation and the copulating gametangia and their suspensors are unequal in size.

6. *Spermatization*   Spermatization is noticed in some Ascomycotina, e.g., *Neurospora* and Basidiomycotina, e.g., *Puccinia*. Male gametangia are very much reduced and are not formed. Instead the minute conidia act like male gametes and are called spermatia. Spherical or rod-shaped male cells are produced from short erect structures, known as spermatiophores (Gr. *spermation* = little seed + *phoreus* = bearer). Spermatia differ from the miroconidia or conidia in their inability to germinate and give rise to a new thallus. The female sex organ may be a female gametangium or a specialized receptive hypha or even a somatic hypha. The spermatia are carried to the female sex organ through wind, water, insect, etc. When it comes in contact with the female sex organ, the cross walls dissolve and the spermatium empties its contents through a pore. Plasmogamy occurs which is followed by karyogamy, i.e., fusion of male and female nuclei in the female sex organ. In *Neurospora*, spermatization has been reported between a conidium and a trichogyne (Figure 1.21).

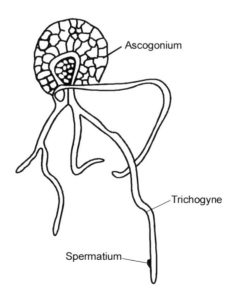

Figure 1.21   Spermatization (*Neurospora crassa*)

7. *Somatogamy* This is the most advanced and specialized type of sexual reproduction where there is total elimination of the formation of both the male and female sex organs. There is fusion between undifferentiated vegetative cells and is called somatic copulation or somatogamy. It is commonly found in Ascomycotina and Basidiomycotina. Two vegetative hyphae from mycelia of opposite strains (+ and –) come in contact and fuse. The nuclei of one migrate into the other and result in the formation of dikaryon (Figure 1.22).

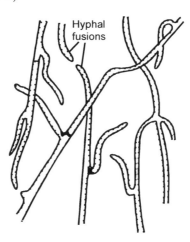

Figure 1.22 Somatic copulation (*Schizophyllum commune*)

Karyogamy In lower fungi, the two compatible nuclei may undergo fusion immediately to form a diploid nucleus. In Ascomycotina and Basidiomycotina they form a dikaryotic (*n* + *n*) association which is extended for varying periods in different fungi. Thus a dikaryotic phase is established.

Meiosis The diploid nucleus in lower fungi undergoes meiosis immediately or after a period of rest and produces zoospores. Meiosis in Ascomycotina and Basidiomycotina occurs in asci and basidia respectively. The products of meiosis, viz., ascospores and basidiospores are haploid and they germinate to give rise to the haploid mycelium.

Hormonal involvement in sexual reproduction The involvement of hormones in the sexual reproduction of fungi was first proposed by de Bary (1881) in *Achlya*. Van den Ende (1976) defined sexual hormone as a diffusible substance playing a specific role in the sexual reproduction of the organism that produces it. There are good evidences of the involvement of sexual hormones in all groups of fungi. These hormones include sirenin, antheridiol, oogoniol, trisporic acid, α-factor. These are not similar in chemical structure.

Sirenin In Allomyces belonging to Blastocladiales, sexual reproduction requires the fusion between uniflagellate motile male and female gametes. Machlis (1958,1966) and his collaborators have shown that the male gametes are attracted to female gametangia by the production of a chemical factor called sirenin. Sirenin, produced by the female gametangia and female gametes, is a sperm attractant and is released into the surrounding water. Male gametes under the influence of this hormone start collecting around the female gametangia and thus sexual fusion was brought about. Sirenin is very active at very low concentration less than 10^{-10} g ml^{-1}

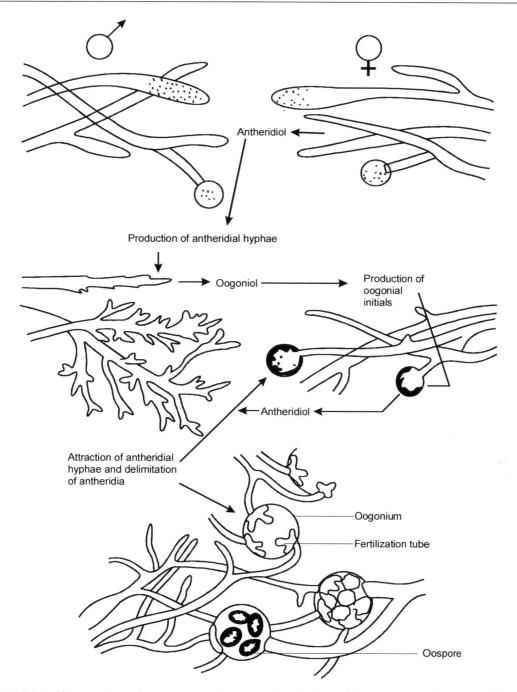

Figure 1.23 Hormonal regulation of sexual reproduction in *A. ambisexualis* involving antheridiol and oogoniol (after van den Ende. 1976)

Antheridiol and oogoniol J.R. Raper (1939–1959) demonstrated a multi-hormonal regulatory system in *Achlya ambisexualis* and *A. bisexualis*. He envisaged four hormones, named A, B, C and D but now it has been proved that only two hormones, viz., antheridiol and oogoniol are involved (Figure 1.23).

Antheridiol Antheridiol elicits the following responses. 1) induction of antheridial hyphae, 2) Chemotrophic stimulation of male hyphae to produce hormone B, 3) delimitation of antheridia.

McMorris and Barksdale (1967) isolated the hormone in a crystalline form and named it antheridiol. It is a steroid and is active at concentrations down to 10^{-10} M. The number of antheridial branches produced in the male hyphae is directly related to the concentration of the hormone (Figure 1.23).

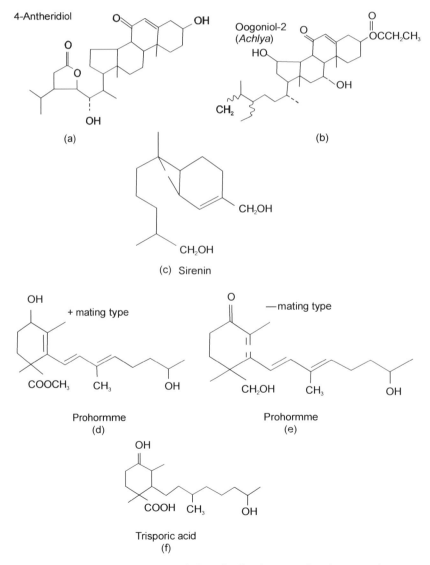

Figure 1.24 (a–f) Structural formulae of chemically characterized are sex hormones in fungi

Oogoniol It is produced by the male isolates in the presence of antheridiol. McMoris and his co-workers (1975) isolated two crystalline compounds from the culture filtrates of *Achlya heterosexualis* which possess hormone B activity. These are steroids and have been named as oogoniol 1, and 2 (Figure 1.24).

Trisporic acid Burgeff (1924) demonstrated sexual hormone in *Mucor mucedo*. Burgeff in a series of experiments proved that a diffusible substance is responsible for the initiation of sexual reproduction in Mucorales. Banbury, (1954) and Plempel (1958) showed that (+) and (–) mycelia of *M. mucedo* when grown together in a liquid culture accumulate substances in the medium that induce zygophores in both mating types of the same fungi. Plempel isolated and purified these substances and were named as trisporic acid B and C. There are three kinds of trisporic acid (such as) A, B and C. Trisporic acid C has the major hormone activity (80%); trisporic acid B has 15%; trisporic acid A shows only 1–2 % of the activity. It is now known that each (+) and (–) strain produces precursor molecules, such as β and γ-carotene which are then converted to trisporic acids (Figure 1.24).

Yeast α-factor There are evidences suggesting the involvement of sexual hormones in the sexual reproduction in *Saccharomyces cerevisiae*. The haploid cells are of two mating types (α and *a*) which conjugate and give rise to diploid cells. Levi (1956) showed that the α cells produce a diffusible chemical which induces the formation of copulatory processes. The *a* cells under the influence of the α factor stop growth and budding and turn into a giant cell. Duntze *et al.* (1970–1973) purified and characterized that α factor; it is a peptide with a molecular weight of 1400 dalton. The peptide is complexed with copper ions.

These two hormones α and *a* hormones are involved in the mating reaction between α and *a* cells. These are steroids. The hormones are active on the opposite mating types and cause swelling of the cells, which is a prerequisite for mating.

Heterokaryosis in Fungi

The term heterokaryosis (*hetero* = dissimilar, *karyosis* = nuclei) has been defined as the coexistence of genetically different nuclei in cytoplasmic continuity with one another. This phenomenon, discovered by Hansen and Smith (1932) in *Botrytis cinerea*, is a speical feature in fungi. Heterokaryosis plays a major role in bringing about variability and sexuality in fungi. It is the pre-requisite for parasexual cycle, in the same way as heterozygosis is for sexual reproduction.

The term heterokaryosis is usually applied to the thallus. In the broader sense, a fungus population, consisting of genetically different individuals is designated as heterokaryotic.

Formation of heterokaryons The heterokaryotic condition arises by the following ways:

1. Mutation
2. Anastomosis
3. Inclusion of dissimilar nuclei in spores after meiosis, in heterothallic fungi.

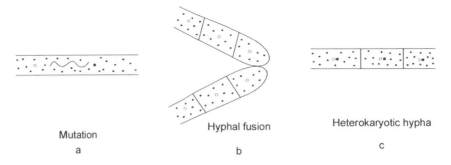

Figure 1.25 (a–c)   Mutation and anastomosis render homokaryotic hyphae heterokaryotic

1. Mutation

A high frequency of mutation, which is characteristic of fungi, is the main source of variability. Mutation frequently renders it heterokaryotic. It has been clearly demonstrated that new races of Phytophthora in USA, in absence of sexual reproduction, have arisen by mutation. Hansen (1938) observed that the single spore of Fusarium by frequent mutations produced variants of the wild type in cultures (Figure 1.25a).

2. Anastomosis (Fusion of hyphae)

This is a common feature in fungi, and is certainly a big source of heterokaryosis. In general, fusion is mostly intraspecific, though inter-specific and inter-generic fusions have been reported (Figure 1.25b) Interspecific anastomosis between *Botrytis cinerea* and *B. ricini* was reported by Hansen and Smith (1935).

Nuclear migration from the point of contact to the remainder of the mycelia takes place and gives rise to a heterokaryotic mycelium (Figure 1.25c). Alternatively, hyphal growth may initiate at the point of fusion, containing nuclei derived from both the parent hyphae. In nature, the most familiar example of anastomosis is the development of dikaryon in Basidiomycotina.

3. Inclusion of dissimilar nuclei in some species

Meiosis results in the reproduction of genetically different nuclei sharing common cytoplasm. In some fungi, e.g., *Neurospora tetrasperma*, *Podospora anserina* and other secondary homothallic fungi, dissimilar nuclei are contained in the same spore, which on germination gives rise to a heterokaryotic thallus. In the asexual phase, this occurs frequently in the multinucleate spores.

Significance of Heterokaryosis

1. Substitute for Heterozyosis and variability

Heterokaryosis provides a substitute for heterozygocity rather than for sex. It is important for maintaining variability (by virtue of the presence of genetically dissimilar nuclei), rather than creating it, which occurs during sexual reproduction by genetic recombination. Hansen and Smith (1932) in *Botrytis cinerea* visualized the heterokaryons and the separation of the different nuclei during conidial formation as substitutes for syngamy and meiosis. Much of the variability assigned to heterokaryosis by Hansen and Smith, however, has been demonstrated, since then, to be due to cytoplasmic factors (Jinks, 1959). Thus, heterozygosis is a substitute for heterozygocity, rather than for sex. The variability gained through heterokaryosis provides plasticity to the fungi to face the environment with greater success.

2. Heterokaryosis and Pathogenicity

Heterokaryosis plays an important role in the pathogenic activities of rusts and smuts. It is essential for pathogenicity in smuts. In heteroecious rusts, heterokaryotic dikaryotic condition is essential for infection of one group of hosts.

3. Origin of New Races

Nelson *et al* (1955) inoculated a resistant wheat variety with different races of rust, which individually failed to cause infection. Lesions appeared after sometime. It was made possible by anastomosis between the inoculated races, which resulted in the origin of a new pathogenic race. Similar origin of new races of rusts has been suggested in *Melampsora tini*. Fusion of urediniospare germ tubes has been seen in various rust fungi and has been taken as indication of the origin of new races. However, recent studies suggest that mechanisms other than simple nuclear exchanges may be frequently involved in the vegetative origin of new races.

4. An initial step in parasexual cycle

Heterokaryosis is an integral, first step of parasexual cycle. But all heterokaryotic fungi are not necessarily parasexual.

Heterothallism in Fungi

On the basis of sex, fungi are divided into three types:

- ◉ Monoecious or hermaphrodites
- ◉ Dioecious
- ◉ Sexually undifferentiated

In monoecious forms, the thallus is of one type and the sex organs are formed from the same thallus and may be compatible or incompatible. In dioecious forms, the thallus is of two types and are called heterothallic. In some Basidiomycetes the thallus is undifferentiated and the same thallus has (+) and (–) strained nuclei.

The term compatibility refers to the fusing capacity of the mycelium. The two fusing elements are said to be compatible. With respect to compatibility, the thalli are of two types namely, homothallic and heterothallic. The homothallic mycelium is self-fertile and is sexually self-compatible. The sex organs produced by the same mycelium may undergo fusion to form the zygote nucleus. The heterothallic forms are self-sterile. It requires the help of another compatible mycelium for sexual reproduction. The two compatible mycelia are designated as plus (+) and minus (–) strain mycelia. Sexual fusion occurs only when two compatible mycelia are mated. This phenomenon has been termed **heterothallism** by Blakeslee (1904).

A.F. Blakeslee, an American geneticist, in 1904, observed that while some species of *Rhizopus* formed zygospores freely, others like *R. stolonifer* formed these only rarely. He examined zygospore formation in Mucorales and discovered the phenomenon of heterothallism in fungi. When two isolates of *R. stolonifer* were grown in a Petri dish, zygospores appeared at the point of contact between hyphae of the two isolates. Blakeslee called these fungi as heterothallic fungi. He designated the two isolates as the (+) and (–) strains since their gametangia were morphologically similar and indistinguishable as male and female gametangia (Figure 1.26).

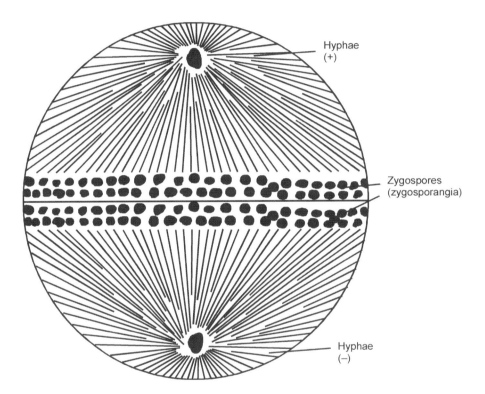

Figure 1.26 *Mucor hiemalis.* a heterothallic fungus growing in a culture plate showing the formation of zygospores (zygosporangia) along the junction of the (+) and (–) mycelia

In the heterothallic species compatibility is determined by the genetic make-up of the nuclei of the mycelium.

The nuclei of one mating type have gene 'A' and the nuclei of the other mating type have gene 'a'.

Heterothallism is of three types, viz., bipolar heterothallium, tetrapolar heterothallism and octopolar heterothallism.

1. *Bipolar heterothallism*   In this, compatibility is governed by a pair of alleles (A and a) located at the single locus on different chromosomes. Fungi in this category have two mating types, each containing genetically different nuclei. It is also called two-allele heterothallism. Gametes or hyphae carrying the (+) and (–) nuclei only can fuse and effect fertilization.

	A	a
A	AA –	AA +
a	AA –	AA +

Bipolar multiple allele heterothallism   This type of heterothallism is controlled by multiple alleles at a singe locus, instead of a pair of alleles. The multiple alleles can be designated as A_1, A_2, A_3, A_4, A_{12}, etc. The meiotic products give rise to thalli of several mating types. The thallus containing the allele 'A', can mate with the 'a' thallus of any mating type except A_1. It is characteristic of Basidiomycotina.

	A_1	A_2	A_3	A_4
A_1	–	+	+	+
A_2	+	–	+	+
A_3	+	+	–	+
A_4	+	+	+	–

2. *Tetrapolar multiple allele heterothallism*   This type of heterothallism is found in basidiomycotina, excepting the rusts. It involves only incompatability factors and therefore, sex organs are not formed. The incompatibility factors are present at two loci, A and B on different chromosomes. Each locus comprises of multiple alleles, as many as 100 or even more. In *Schizophyllum commune*, 122 alleles of A and 61 of B factor have been identified in laboratory. The A and B allelic incompatibility factors segregate independently at meiosis and give rise to thalli of numerous mating types. Mating occurs between thalli which have nuclei carrying different alleles at both loci. The diploid nucleus comes to have the alleles A_1, B_1, A_2, B_2.

In this type of heterothallism the outbreeding is complete, (100%) against 25% in bipolar. This is due to enormous increase in the number of the possible mating type of the thalli.

Flat and Barrage Reactions   When two thalli with a common A or B alleles are mated, though plasmogamy takes place and heterokaryons are formed, fruiting never occurs. If the heterokaryons have common A alleles (and dissimilar B alleles), the mating is termed flat reaction. Such heterokaryons show poor growth; hyphae are curly and irregularly branched. Parag (1965) reported that the presence of common A alleles prevent formation of clamp connections; disrupt nuclear distribution and also cause morphological and metabolic abnormalities. The mating between thalli containing similar B alleles (but different A alleles), show what is called a barrage reaction. The hyphae at the point of contact show cessation of growth, resulting in a "barrage" or "3 one of no growth" between the colonies of the two thalli. Common B factors, thus prevent karyogamy and meiosis (Figure 1.27).

	A_1B_1	A_1B_2	A_2B_1	A_2B_2
A_1B_1	–	FL	B	+
A_1B_2	FL	–	+	B
A_2B_1	B	+	–	FL
A_2B_2	+	B	FL	–

Figure 1.27 Mating reactions between the four possible isolates of a tetrapolar fungus. (+, compatible cross;–, incompatible cross; FL, flat reaction; B, barrage reaction)

3. *Octopolar heterothallism*   In ocotopolar heterothallism, sexual compatibility is governed by three pairs of factors Aa, Bb and Cc which are located at two different loci on different chromosomes, e.g., some members of Basidiomycotina.

4. *Tetra polar heterothallism*   In this, sexual compatibility is governed by two pairs of factors such as A a and B b which are located at two different loci on different chromosomes.

Parasexuality in Fungi

For a long time, sexual reproduction was thought to be the only mechanism of achieving genetic recombination. One alternative method of sexual reproduction was discovered in fungi *(Aspergillus nidu-lans)* by Pontecoro and Raper in 1952 and they named it as the parasexual cycle. In this, genetic recombination is achieved through mitotic crossing over and haploidization. In this cycle, plasmogamy, karyogamy and meiosis do occur in a regular sequence and at regular intervals. Karyogamy and meiosis are not bound by space and time. This phenomenon is now reported in several fungi belonging to Ascomycotina and Basidiomycotina.

The steps of parasexual cycle   The parasexual cycle occurs in the four following steps.

1. Establishment of heterokaryosis
2. Formation of heterozygous diploids
3. Multiplication of the diploid nuclei and occasional mitotic crossing over
4. Occasional haploidization through aneuploidy

1. *Establishment of heterokaryosis*   The presence of haploid nuclei of dissimilar genotype in the same cytoplasm is a prerequisite for recombination. This is achieved by heterokaryosis which is brought about by mutation and anastomosis between hyphae of different origin. This step is equivalent to plasmogamy of sexual reproduction.

2. *Formation of heterozygous diploids*   The nuclear fusions between dissimilar nuclei result in the formation of heterozygous diploid nucleus. It is a rare event occurring at the rate of one in a million. The heterozygous diploid nuclei which are fairly stable, by multiplication and sorting out through conidia, give rise to diploid thalli. The diploid colonies are recognized by higher DNA content of the nucleus, the bigger size of the conidia and certain phenotypic characteristics of the colony. This is a prolonged diploid

phase which enhances the chances of mitotic crossing over.

3. *Multiplication of the diploid nuclei and occasional mitotic crossing over* This is the most important key event in parasexual cycle where genetic recombination takes place. In *Aspergillus nidulans* mitotic crossing over occurs rarely with a frequency of 10^{-20} per nuclear division. New heterozygous recombinant haploid nuclei are formed which was subsequently proved cytologically.

4. *Occasional haploidization through aneuploidy* The diploid nuclei give rise to haploid nuclei by gradual loss of chromosomes during successive mitotic division (aneuploidy). This is called haploidization and meiosis is not involved. It occurs at a constant frequency of 10^{-3} per nuclear division. The aneuploid nuclei can be represented as $(2n-1)$ at the beginning and $(2n-n)$, i.e., (n) or haploid, at the end. The aneuploids are genetically unstable, and once the loss of chromosomes has started, the selection favours the development of the fully balanced haploid nuclei (Figure 1.28).

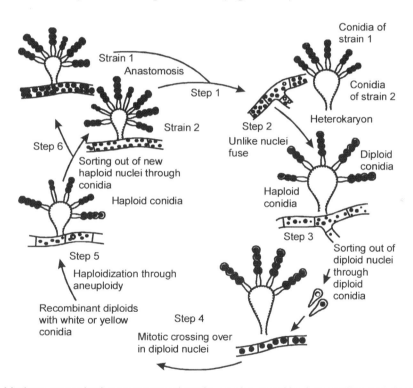

Figure 1.28 Various steps in the parasexual cycle as observed in *Aspergillus nidulans* and asexual state of *Emericella nidulans* (Adapted from Pontecorvo, 1955)

Fruit bodies in Fungi

Any fruit body which produces the spores is called a sporocarp. Majority of Ascomycotina and Basidiomycotina produce fruit bodies of various sizes and shapes and are called ascocarps and basidiocarps respectively. Fruit bodies are not formed by aquatic fungi. Fruit bodies are the post-fertilization products and are always formed after post-fertilization changes.

Types of ascocarps   Ascocarp is the fruit body of Ascomycotina. Generally the ascocarp contains the asci formed from more than one neighbouring ascogonia. The following types are recognized.

1. *Cleistothecium*   It is a small, hollow, more or less globose indehiscent ascocarp without an opening or ostiole, e.g., Plectomycetes. The cleistothecium may be sessile or stalked. The fruit wall or peridium may consist of loosely interwoven hyphae or pseudoparenchyma. It may be smooth or sometimes covered with hyphal outgrowth called appendages which may be of various types. The asci are globose or ellipsoidal and lie scattered at different levels within the peridium, e.g., *Penicillium* and *Aspergillus*. The ascal wall is evanescent, i.e., it degenerates at maturity and the ascospores are liberated into the cavity of the ascocarp. In some fungi like *Erysiphe*, the asci are arranged regularly and form a distinct hymenium. The ascus bears eight or more ascospores endogenously, which are liberated by the decay or irregular splitting of the wall of the asci and the cleistothecium (Figure 1.29 a–c).

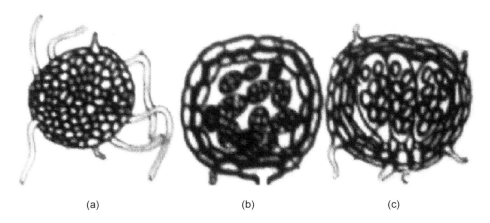

(a)　　　　　　　　(b)　　　　　　　　(c)

Figure 1.29   (a–c) Ascomycetes. (a) Entire cleistothecium bearing hyphal appendages; (b) Section of a cleistothecium of *Aspergillus* with scattered asci; (c) L.S. cleistothecium of *Erysiphe* with asci forming a regular layer

2. *Perithecium*   It is a small, rounded or flask-shaped structure formed in Pyrenomycetes—*Neurospora*. At maturity it has a definite apical pore or opening or ostiole through which the ascospores escape. The ostiole may simply be a short papilla opening by a circular pore. In many species it is in the form of a long neck with an apical pore. The ostiolar canal is lined by slender, short, delicate hairlike sterile outgrowths called the periphysis. They point outwards and they regulate the movement of ascospores during discharge. The wall of the perithecium is peridium and it encloses a perithecial cavity which is internally lined by the hymenium either throughout or only at the base. The hymenium consists of club-shaped or cylindrical asci intermingled with paraphyses which are sterile. The ascal wall is persistent and each ascus produces a limited number of ascospores (Figure 1.30 a–b).

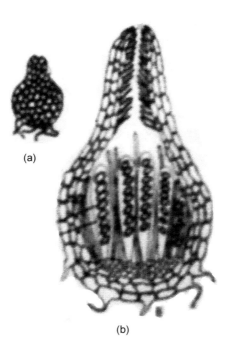

(a)

(b)

Figure 1.30 (a–b) Ascomycetes. a, Entire perithecium; b, V.S. of perithecium showing structure

3. *Apothecium*   It is a disc or saucer-shaped or cup-shaped structure formed in Discomycetes—*Peziza*. It may be sessile or stalked (Figure 1.31 a and b).

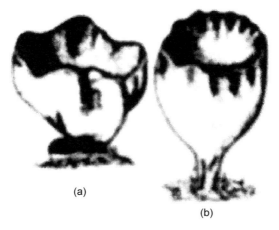

(a)

(b)

Figure 1.31 (a–b) Ascomycetes. Two apothecia; (a) Sessile apothecium of *Peziza*; (b) stalked apothecium of *Umula*

It is an open type of fruit body and consists of three parts, namely hymenium, hypothecium and excipulum (Figure 1.32).

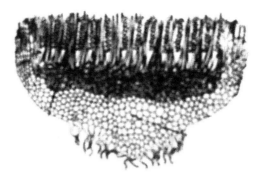

Figure 1.32   Ascomycetes. V.S. of apothecium showing structural details

i. **Hymenium**   This lines the cavity of the cup and is called the thecium. It is the fertile layer and it is palisade-like with many tubular or cylindrical asci intermingled with sterile paraphysis. The paraphyses are slender, separate hyphae and sometimes they form a layer above the thecium and is called epithecium. Paraphyses have a protective, supporting and distributing role. The mature asci are tubular or club-shaped with a persistent ascal wall and eight ascospores.

ii. **Hypothecium**   This lies immediately beneath the hymenium. It consists of a network of hyphae running horizontal to the hymenium from which the asci and paraphyses arise.

iii. **Excipulum**   This makes the base and sides of the apothecium and it forms the bulk of the apothecium. It is made up of pseudoparenchyma. The outer layers of the excipulum constitute the ectal excipulum which is protective in function and the inner portion is the medullary excipulum which is supportive and nutritive in function. (Figure 1.32).

4. *Ascostroma*   It is a stromatic ascocarp with many locules or cavities and is formed in Loculoascomycetes. The asci are bitunicate, covered with two layers. The stroma is a mass or a cushion of compactly woven somatic hyphae which form the wall of the ascocarp. It produces a single or many locules which may open at the surface of the stroma by openings. Each locule may have a single ascus (monoascal) or more than one asci (polyascal). In many species the upper part of the stroma disintegrates and the asci are exposed thereby liberating the ascospores (Figure 1.33).

Figure 1.33 Ascomycetes. L.S. of mature ascostroma of *Mycosphaerella tulipiferae* showing apical pore and basal group of asci in the locule

5. *Thyriothecium*   It is like an inverted apothecium formed in Microthyriales.

6. *Hysterothecium*   It is a small black elongated boat-shaped fruit body with a leathery or hard texture, and is found in Hysteriales. The fruit body opens at maturity by a single long narrow slit which runs parallel to the long axis of the fruit body from top to bottom. In a cross section, it looks like a perithecium and in a longitudinal section, it looks like an apothecium (Figure 1.34 a and b).

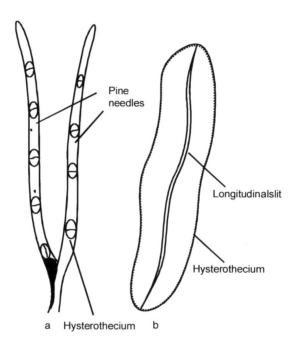

a   Hysterothecium   b

Figure 1.34   (a) Pine needles with hysterothecia; (b) Single hysterothecium (After Higgins)

Types of basidiocarps   Basidiocarps are formed in Homobasidiomycetes and are large massive complex structures. They may be microscopic or macroscopic. The basidiocarps are borne on the mycelial strands of the secondary mycelium. The basidiocarp produces many basidia. Each basidium forms two to four basidiopores at the tips of sterigmata and the basidiospores are obliquely placed on the sterigmata which facilitates the easy discharge of basidiospore. The basidia may be formed in hymenia in the series Hymenomycetes (Agaricales and Polyporales) or in gleba in Gastromycetes (Lycoperdales, Sclerodermatales, Phallales and Nidulariales).

Agaricales   In *Agaricus* or mushroom, the basidiocarp has a stalklike portion, the stripe and an umbrella-shaped cup, the pileus. From the underside of the pileus, many thin vertical strips or plates of tissue called the gills or lamellae hang down (Figure 1.35). The outer surface of the gill is lined by hymenium which is formed of fertile cells called basidia and sterile structures called basidiola and paraphysis. The gills are of different lengths. Each basidium produces two to four basidiospores at the tips of sterigmata. The gills are fleshy and edible.

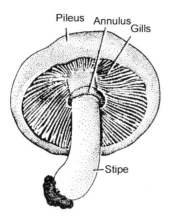

Figure 1.35 A mature fruiting body of *Agaricus campestris*

Polyporales These are wood-rotting fungi and form a woody, corky or leathery fruit body on the surface of wood. The basidiocarp is differentiated into a short stalk or stipe which is terminated by a rounded caplike structure, the pileus (Figure 1.36). The upper surface of the pileus is flat and the lower surface of the pileus bears numerous fine pores. Each pore is the opening of the small tube. The inner hollow surface of the tube is lined by a fertile layer called hymenium. The hymenium is made up of fertile cells called the basidia and sterile structures called the cystidia. The basidiospores which escape through the pore are dispersed by air and insects.

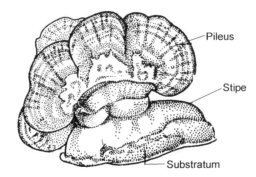

Figure 1.36 Basidiocarps of *Polyporus sulphureus*

Sclerodermatales The fruit bodies are sessile, round and flat. The peridium is hard, rough and thick and the gleba is powdery without any capillitium. The basidiospores have a thick, spiny, reticulate or ornamental wall.

Lycoperdales The fertile part of the basidiocarp is called the gleba and it is powdery. Lycoperdon, the fruit body is called puffball and the basidiocarp is globose, pear-shaped, ovoid and fleshy when young. At maturity the basidia and hyphae undergo autodigestion. Thus the gleba in turned into a powdery mass consisting of light basidiospores intermixed with capillitia. It is surrounded by a thick peridium which ruptures or opens by one or more pores though which the basidiospores are puffed out (Figure 1.37 a–c).

In *Geastram* (earthstar) the peridium is three-layered. The exoperidium at maturity splits from top downwards into lobes which turn outward and look like rays of a star. The exposed endoperidium develops an apical pore. The basidia are capitates; capillitium is made up of unseptate branched hyphae [Figure 1.38(a–b)].

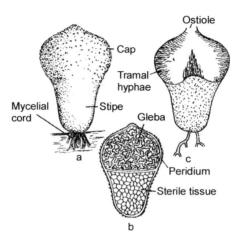

Figure 1.37 (a–c) *Lycoperdon perlatum.* (a) The mature fruit body, the cap is covered by fragile spines; (b) Same in longitudinal section showing chambers lined with hymenium; (c) Capillitium threads in dry condition

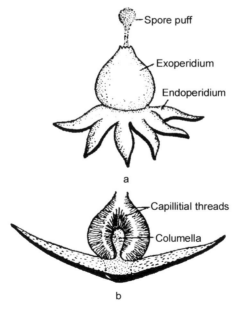

Figure 1.38 (a – b) *Geastrum sp.* (a) Expanded fruit body looks like a star; (b) Vertical section through the fruit body showing sheafs of capillitium threads attached to the wall and the columella

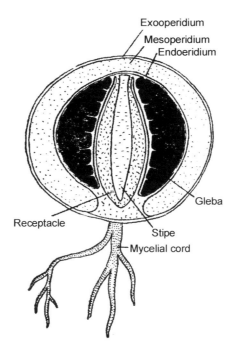

Figure 1.39 *Phallus impudicus*, vertical section of full-grown "egg"

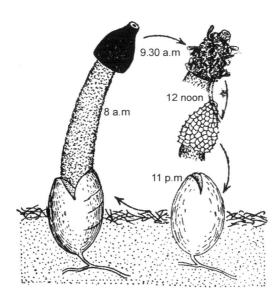

Figure 1.40 *P. impudicus*, showing emergence of fruit body and spore dispersal through insects

Phallales These are commonly called stink-horns. Basidiocarps stink like decaying flesh during and after the exposure of the gleba. The fruit body is pileate and the mature gleba is fleshy and slimy

(Figure 1.39). The slimy basidiospores are dispersed by insects. In *Phallus* the peridium is three-layered consisting of a papery exo-and endoperidium and a thick gelatinous mesoperidium. The young gleba contains several cavities lined by basidia with basidiospores. When the basidia are ripe, the gleba undergoes autodigestion to form a slimy mass in which the basidiospores are suspended. The stipe elongates and bursts out of the peridium carrying the pileus and gleba at its apex. The gleba secretes a sugary substance, which attracts insects like blue beetles and green beetles, and they devour the slimy mass with gleba (Figure 1.40).

Nidulariales   These are called the "Bird's nest fungi" since the fruit body looks like a nest containing the eggs. The gleba is divided into several hard structures called peridioles (Figure 1.41). The peridioles are attached to the peridium. In *Cyathus* the basidiocarp looks like an inverted bell with many hanging peridioles. The peridiole is attached to the peridium by means of a mycelial cord called funiculus. The funiculus is made of three portions—sheath, middle piece and purse. The sheath is attached to the inner wall of the peridium. Middle piece connects the sheath to the purse. The purse contains funicular cord with a lower sticky end called hapteron. The fertile part of the peridiole is surrounded by a thick wall called tunica. The inner layer of the tunica is lined with club-shaped basidia on which the basidiospores are borne (Figure 1.42).

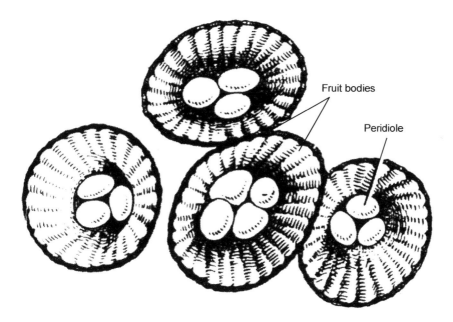

Fruit bodies

Peridiole

Figure 1.41   Mature fruit bodies of *Cyathus* containing peridioles

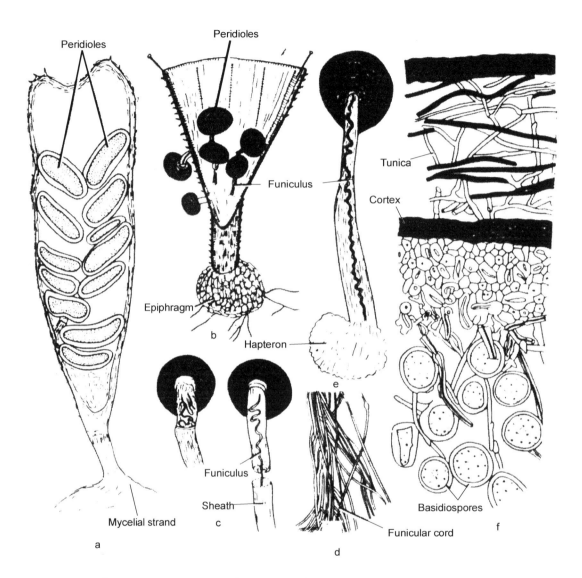

Figure 1.42 (a–f)   Cyathus. (a–b) Structure of mature fruit body showing various parts, (c–e) Single peridiole (e–f) T.S of a peridiole

In *Sphaearobolus*, the fruit body is spherical. It has a gleba surrounded by a six-layered peridium. When the peridium splits, it splits into two cups one fitting inside the other but in contact only at the margins. The outer cup is derived from the three outer layers of the pleridium and the inner cup from the subsequent two layers. The sixth layer is digested to form a fluid so that the glebal mass is loosely placed inside the inner cup. The inner cup is made of turgid tissues which absorb water and turns inside out with a great speed shooting the glebal mass to a long distance (up to 7 m). Ingold (1967) referred this fungus as the most powerful piece of fungal artillary (Figre 1.43a and b).

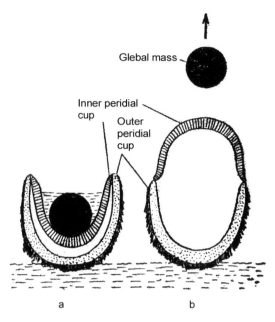

Figure 1.43 (a and b) *Sphaerobolus stellatus*. (a) LS. of an open sporophore before discharge of spores; (b) Same at the moment of discharge of the gelatinous mass

LIFE CYCLES IN FUNGI

Many fungi, like other sexually reproducing organisms, show an alternation between haploid and diploid nuclear phases in their life cycles. The haploid phase begins with the completion of meiosis and the diploid phase starts with the fusion of the haploid nuclei during sexual reproduction. In many higher Ascomycotina and Basidiomycotina, a third phase, the dikaryophase intervenes the haploid and diploid phases. The dikaryophase is represented by the dikaryotic mycelium with the cells containing the dikaryon. The dikaryons are the pairs of nuclei derived from the two opposite mating types during sexual reproduction. A life cycle involving the dikaryons is found only in fungi. Raper (1954) described seven basic types of life cycles in fungi. These are:

1. *Asexual cycle* The entire group of fungi imperfecti (Deuteromycotina) shows this type of life cycle. There is no alternation of haploid and diploid phase. The diploid (2n) phase is lacking.

2. *Haploid cycle* The life cycle is completely haploid (n); the diploid phase is restricted to the zygote nucleus. This type of life cycle is found in majority of lower fungi, e.g., *Saprolegnia, Ascomycotina.*

3. *Haploid cycle with restricted dikaryon* This type of life cycle is found in higher Ascomycotina forming dikaryotic ($n + n$) ascogenous hyphae, which are completely dependent on the haploid mycelium. This is predominantly a haploid life cycle but it differs in the separation of plasmogamy from karyogamy in time and space. The gametic nuclei pair to form dikaryons which multiply by conjugate or simultaneous mitotic divisions in the ascogenous hyphae. The dikaryons finally undergo karyogamy and meiosis in the ascal primordia, e.g., *Neurospora.*

4. *Haploid dikaryotic cycle*   Most of the Basidiomycotina exhibit this type of life cycle in which the dikaryophase (*n* + *n*) is more extensive and also independent of the haploid phase. The cycle comprises two roughly equivalent phases and terminates in a single diploid nuclear generation represented by the diploid zygote nucleus.

5. *Dikaryotic cycle*   The complete life cycle is passed in dikaryotic phase and both the haploid and diploid generations are represented by a single nuclear generation. The immediate products of meiosis, viz., the ascopores or the basidiospores, fuse to initiate the dikaryotic phase which persists until karyogamy occurs, e.g., smut fungi.

6. *Haploid—diploid cycle*   This type of life cycle occurs in two groups of fungi, viz., the Blastocladiales—*Allomyces* and Endomycetales—*Saccharomyces*. Both the haploid and diploid phases are prominent in the life cycle and thus the life cycle shows isomorphic alternation of generation like that of algae.

7. *Diploid cycle*   This type of life cycle is completely diploid and the haploid phase is restricted to the gametes or the immediate products of meiosis. It is known to occur in yeasts like *Saccharomyces cerevisiae*, in the Myxomycetes or true slime moulds and many oomycetous fungi.

CLASSIFICATION OF FUNGI

There are nearly 1,00,000 species of fungi in the world. Taxon is the general term for any taxonomic group whatever it ranks. The various taxa have standard endings according to the International Code of Nomenclature.

Taxa	Standard endings
Division	Mycota
Subdivision	Mycotina
Class	Mycetes
Subclass	Mycetidae
Order	Ales
Family	Aceae

The well-known classification for fungi proposed by Ainsworth (1966) was given in the Dictionary of Fungi (1971). An advanced Treatise (Ainsworth, 1973) may be considered as an ideal scheme of classification that reflects natural relationship in this system. The fungi with plasmodia or pseudoplasmodia are classified in the division Myxomycota whereas most of the remaining filamentous fungi are classified in division Eumycota. Recently John Webster (1980) also chose to adopt the scheme proposed by Ainsworth (1973). Ainsworth (1973) treated fungi as a separate kingdom with two divisions; the Myxomycota for plasmodial forms; and the Eumycota, for non-plasmodial forms which are frequently mycelial. The division Myxomycota includes the slime molds in which the thallus is a non-green, multinucleate mass of protoplasm called the plasmodium. The plamodium lacks a definite cell wall and thus is amoeboid in shape. It is free living, diploid and holocarpic. The division Myxomycota has four classes such as Acrasiomycetes, Hydromyxomycetes, Myxomycetes and Plasmodiophoromycetes. The division Eumycota was futher divided into five subdivisions such as Mastigomycotina, Zygomycotina, Ascomycotina, Basidiomycotina and Deuteromycotina. This division is based on the presence or absence of motile cells, perfect-state spores and the type of perfect-state spores. Fungi which produce motile zoospores are placed under the subdivision Mastigomycotina. On the basis of number (one or two), position (anterior, posterior or lateral) and type (whiplash or tinsel) of the flagella on the zoopores, the subdivision Mastigomycotina is divided into three classes: Chytridiomycetes, Hyphochytridiomycetes and Oomycetes. The subdivision Zygomycotina consits of two classes: Zygomycetes and Trichomycetes. This subdivision includes coenocytic fungi which lack motile cells and produce zygospores as the perfect or sexual spores.

The subdivision Ascomycotina is divided into six classes: Hemiascomycetes, Loculoascomycetes, Plectomycetes, Laboulbeniomycetes, Pyrenomycetes and Discomycetes. The primitive genera lacking ascocarp and ascogenous hyphae are segregated under class Hemiascomycetes. The rest which form ascogenous hyphae and ascocarps are placed in the other five classes. The subdivision Basidiomycotina comprises of three classes: Teliomycetes, Hymenomycetes and Gastromycetes. This division is based on the presence or absence of the basidiocarp, type of basidiocarp, septate or unseptate nature of the basidia and the explosive or passive discharge of the basidiospores. The subdivision Deuteromycotina is divided into three classes: Blastomycetes, Hyphomycetes and Coelomycetes. This division is based upon the presence or absence of mycelium and the types of asexual fructifications. This scheme of classification is given below.

KINGDOM FUNGI

Key to divisions of fungi

Plasmodium or pseudoplasmodium present	Myxomycota I
Plasmodium or pseudoplasmodium absent, assimilative phase typically filamentous	Eumycota II

I. Myxomycota

Key to classes of Myxomycota

1.	Assimilative phase free-living amoebae which unite as a pseudoplasmodium before reproduction	Acrasiomycetes
	Assimilative phase a plasmodium	
2.	Plasmodium form ing a net work ("net plasmodium")	Hydromyxomycetes
	Plasmodium not forming a net work	
3.	Plasmodium saprobic, free-living	Myxomycetes
	Plasmodium parasitic within cells of the host plant	Plasmodiophoromycetes

II. Eumycota

Key to subdivisitions of Eumycota

1.	Motile cells (zoospores) present, perfect state spores typically oospores	Mastigomycotina III
	Motile cells absent	
2.	Perfect state absent	Deuteromycotina VII
	Perfect state present	
3.	Perfect state spores zygospores	Zygomycotina IV
	Zygospores absent	
4.	Present-state spores ascospores	Ascomycotina V
	Perfect-state spores basidiospores	Basidiomycotina VI

III. Mastigomycotina

Key to classes of Mastigomycotina

1.	Zoospores posteriorly uniflagellate (flagella whiplash-type)	Chytridiomycetes
	Zoospores not posteriorly uniflagellate	
2.	Zoospores anteriorly uniflagellate (flagella tinsel-type)	Hyphochytridomycetes
	Zoospores biflagellate (posterior flagellum whiplash-type; anterior tinsel type); cell wall cellulosic	Oomycetes

IV. Zygomycotina

Key to classes of Zygomycotina

Saprobic or, if parasitic or predacious, having mycelium immersed in host tissue	Zygomycetes
Associated with arthropods and attached to the cuticle or digestive tract by a holdfast and not immersed in the host tissue	Trichomycetes

V. Ascomycotina

Key to classes of Ascomycotina

1.	Ascocarps and ascogenous hyphae absent; thallus mycelial or yeastlike	Hemisascomycetes
	Ascocarps and ascogenous hyphae present; thallus mycelial	
2.	Asci bitunicate; ascocarp an ascostroma.	Loculoascomycetes
	Asci typically unitunicate; if bitunicate, ascocarp an apothecium	

3. Asci evanescent, scattered within the astomous ascocarp which
    is typically a cleistothecium; ascospores aseptate — Plectomycetes

    Asci regularly arranged within the ascocarps as a basal or peripheral layer

4. Exoparasites of arthropods; thallus reduced; ascocarp a perithecium;
    asci inoperculate — Laboulbeniomycetes

    Not exoparasites of arthropods

5. Ascocarp typically a perithecium which is usually ostiolate
    (if astomous, asci not evanescent); asci inoperculate with an
    apical pore or slit — Pyrenomycetes

    Ascocarp an apothecium or a modified apothecium,
    frequently macrocarpic, epigean or hypogean; asci
    inoperculate or operculate — Discomycetes

VI. Basidiomycotina

Key to classes of Basidiomycotina

1. Basidiocarp lacking and replaced by teliospores or chlamydospores
    (encystedprobasidia) grouped in sori or scattered within the host
    tissue; parasitit on vascular plants — Teliomycetes

    Basidiocarp usually well-developed; basidia typically
    organized as a hymenium; saprobic or rarely parasitic

2. Basidiocarp typically gymnocarpous or semiangiocarpous;
    basidia phragmobasidia (Phragmobasidiomycetidae) or
    holobasidia (Holobasidiomycetidae); basidiospores ballistospores — Hymenomycetes

    Basidiocarp typically angiocarpous; basidia holobasidia;
    basidiospores not ballistospores — Gasteromycetes

VII. Deuteromycotina

Key to classes of Deuteromycotina

1. Budding (yeast or yeast-like) celles with or without pseudomycelium
    charateristic; true mycelium lacking or not well-developed — Blastomycetes

    Mycelium well developed, assimilative budding cells absent

2. Mycelium sterile or bearing spores directly or on special branches
    (sporophores) which may be variously aggregated but not in
    pycnidia or acervuli — Hyphomycetes

    Spores in pycnidia or acervuli — Coelomycetes

CULTURE OF FUNGI

A pure culture of the fungal organism should be raised to study a fungus. For this purpose, a sterile culture medium is used with agar. Agar is used as a jelling agent in liquid culture medium and not as a source of food. 2% malt extract in water is the usual medium which contains all the ingredients essential for fungal growth. The other common media for culturing fungi are potato dextrose agar (PDA) and corn-meal agar media.

Potato dextrose agar (PDA)

Potato (peeled)	-	200.0 g
Dextrose (glucose)	-	20.0 g
Agar	-	20.0 g
Water	-	1000 ml

Malt extract agar (MA)

Malt extract	-	20.0 g
Agar	-	15.0 g
Water	-	1000 ml

Corn-meal agar (CMA)

Ground corn (maize)	-	25.0 g
Peptone (if desired)	-	20.0 g
Glucose (if desired)	-	20.0 g
Agar	-	20.0 g
Water	-	1000 ml

The fungi are usually grown in a glass Petri dish on nutrient agar called the agar plate. Sometimes the fungus is grown on an agar slope. To prepare an agar slope, nutrient agar is poured in test tubes plugged with non-absorbent cotton wool and placed in a slanting manner during cooling and setting of the medium.

The glassware such as test tubes or petri dishes are sterilized in an oven in dry heat at 170°C to 180°C for at least an hour. The nutrient agar containing the medium is placed in a flask. The flask with the medium is plugged with non-absorbent cotton plug and is then sterilized in an autoclave at a pressure of 15–20 pounds per square inch which corresponds to a temperature of 121°C to 126°C. It is maintained for 15 to 20 minutes. The sterilized medium is then cooked to 40°C and poured into the Petri dish and covered with a lid. When the agar is set, the lid is lifted gently in an incubator and the fungus is inoculated with an inoculation needle. The inoculum may be a mycelium or a spore. Then they are placed in an incubator which is kept at a temperature of 37°C for a couple of days during which some of the agar plates will show fungal growth.

ECONOMIC IMPORTANCE OF FUNGI

Fungi, along with bacteria and animals, play an important role in decomposition of complex remains of dead organisms, especially the plant materials. They are thus responsible for release of nutrients back to the soil and atmosphere for plants. Soil fertility is therefore directly related to the activities of fungi. The decomposition of organic material benefits man in three important ways

i.   Organic debris are continuously being removed from man's environment.

ii. Large quantites of CO_2 essential for photosynthesis are released to the atmosphere and made available to the green plants for photosynthesis.

iii. Humus formation is affected to maintain soil fertility.

In addition, fungi are both beneficial and harmful to man in a variety of ways. Their beneficial activities include their edible nature in industry and medicine, their use in fermentation and food processing, and in biological control of plant and human pathogens. They are also beneficial in the deterioration of wood and wood products, paper, textile and leather goods. The harmful activities of fungi include the food spoilage and diseases produced in plants, animals and human beings.

Industrial Uses of Fungi

Fungi have two major uses in industry.

i. as a source of chemicals.

ii. as food and food-processing agents.

Fungi produce a wide range of useful compounds like organic acids, alcohols, enzymes, vitamins, glycerol, lipids, proteins and antibiotics.

i. *Organic acids*   The most important organic acids produced commercially as a result of the biochemical activities of moulds are gallic acid, citric acid, gluconic acid, oxalic acid, fumaric acid and lactic acid. The sources of these organic acids are given in the Table.

Organic acids	Sources
Gallic acid	*Penicillium glaucum*
Citric acid	*Aspergillus niger*
Gluconic acid	*A. niger, Penicillium purpurogenum*
Oxalic acid	*A. niger*
Fumaric acid	*Mucor, Rhizopus*
Lactic acid	*Rhizopus oryzae*

ii. *Alcohol*   Alcohol is the fermentation product of sugar by yeast. It is the basis of two industries, the baking and brewing industry. Fermentation of sugar solution by yeast produces ethyl alcohol and carbon dioxide. In the brewing industry, alcohol is the important product. The baker's and brewer's yeast, *Saccharomyces cerevisiae*, produces the enzyme complex called zymase which converts sugar into alcohol and carbon dioxide. Moulds like *Mucor racemosus, Rhizopus* and *Aspergillus niger* are used as starters to bring about saccharification of starch. Yeast is employed in the second stage to act on the sugar.

iii. *Enzymes*   Many products of high enzymatic activity like taka diastase, digestin and polyzime are produced by *Aspergillus flavum. Aspergillus niger* and *A. oryzae* produce amylase in culture. *Saccharomyces cerevisiae* is used for the extraction of the enzyme invertase.

iv. *Vitamins*   The yeasts are the best sources of vitamin B-complex. Riboflavin is obtained from a filamentous yeast, *Ashbya gossypi.*

v. *Proteins*   The yeasts (*Saccharomyces cerevisiae* and *Candida utilis*) contain high percentage of protein of great nutritive value. They are grown with ammonia as a source of nitrogen and molasses as a source of carbon. The manufactured product is called food yeast. Single cell protein (SCP) is a complete substitute for conventional protein foods. *Penicillium, Fusarium* and *Candida* are now used in the production of SCP on a pilot scale.

vi. *Glycerol and lipids*   Glycerol is obtained from the yeasts. *Aspergillus niger, Absidia, Rhizopus* and *Mortierella* are the sources of lipids.

vii. *Hormones*   Gibberellin, a group of plant hormones which is used to accelerate the growth of many crops, is produced by *Gibberella fujikuroi.*

viii. *Cheese industry*   Certain fungi like *Penicillium camemberti* and *P. roqueforti* are used in the manufacture of cheese. They play a vital role in the refining of cheese and they give cheese a characteristic texture and flavour.

Role of Fungi in Medicine

Some fungi produce substances which help to cure diseases caused by pathogenic microorganisms. These substances are called the antibiotics. These are produced when the main phase of growth is over and thus they are called the secondary metabolites.

The role of fungi in producing antibiotic substances was first established by Sir Alexander Fleming in 1929. The antibiotic drug, Penicillin, was extracted from *Penicillium notatum*. It was the first antibiotic to be widely used. Penicillin is now produced on a commercial scale from the improved strains of *P. notatum* and *P. chrysogenum*.

Streptomycin is obtained from *Streptomyces griseus*. Some of the Actinomycetes are the sources of many antibiotics such as Chloromycetin, Aureomycin and Terramycin. They inhibit the growth of many pathogenic bacteria and are used in the treatment of many viral diseases.

Griseofulvin produced from the mycelium of *Penicillium griseofulvum* has antifungal properties. It acts on the hyphae by, interfering with wall formation. It is effective against fungal skin diseases such as ringworm and athletes foot disease.

Ergot is the sclerotium produced in the ovaries of the flowers of grasses (rye) infected with *Claviceps purpurea*. Ergot is used in veterinary and human medicine. Ergot contains several alkaloids like ergonovine, ergometrin and ergotamine. These are used in rapid and powerful contraction of the uterus. It is also used to control bleeding during childbirth. A derivative of ergot known as lysergic acid (LSD) is used in experimental psychiatry.

The giant puff-ball, *Calvatia*, contains an anti-cancer substance called calvacin. This prevents stomach tumour.

Fungi as Food

The edible fungi are mostly the mushrooms. Most of the species of *Agaricus* are edible. The other edible mushrooms are *Pleurotus, Tremella, Volvariella, Coprinus* and *Morchella*. In India *Agaricus, Volvariella* and *Pleurotus* are cultivated on a large scale and sold in markets.

Mushrooms are rich in proteins (20–35% proteins of dry wt. basis) which is higher than in many vegetables and fruits. They are also good sources of vitamin C and B-complex particularly thiamin, riboflavin and niacin. Folic acid and vitamin B_{12} are also present in mushroom. Mushrooms are ideal for diabetic persons since they are low in starch/sugar content and high in protein content. An essential fatty acid called linoleic acid is present in mushrooms. Since they do not produce cholesterol, they are good for heart patients. Due to their alkaline ash, high potassium–sodium ratio and high fibre content, mushrooms are ideal food for those suffering from hypertension, from hyper-acidity and constipation.

Fungi in Fermentation and Food Processing

Asian and oriental foods and drinks based on fungal fermentation include tempeh, soya sauce, shoyu, Japanese sake (rice wine), Miso or soy cheese.

i. **Tempeh** It is produced in large quantities in Indonesia and New Guinea. Soybeans have a high protein content but they are difficult to digest. If such foods are fermented by fungi they are made palatable. Dehulled soybean grits are soaked in water for 2 hours at 50°C, cooked for 30 min., drained and cooled. The beans are inoculated with spores of *Rhizopus oligosporus*, packed in trays and incubated at 31°C for 20–24 hours. It forms a solid cake and the cooled slice is like bread.

ii. **Shoyu (Soya sauce)** The starting material is soybeans and wheat. It is a dark brownish liquid with a distinct pleasant aroma. It is widely used for adding flavour to many foods and for seasoning.

iii. **Miso or soy cheese** Miso is a food prepared by a two-step fermentation process. The first involves the fermentation of rice to produce enzymes followed by a second fermentation of the mouldy rice along with soyabeans, salt and suitable inoculum. The moulds used for this fermentation are *Aspergillus oryzae* and *Saccharomyces rouxii*.

Fungi in Biological Control

Biological control may be defined as any method of control that involves biological rather than physical or chemical methods. Some fungi are antagonistic to and hyper-parasitic on other fungi as well as bacteria, nematodes and insects which are serious plant pathogens. These fungi are used as agents of biological control of diseases. For example, *Trichoderma harzianum* has been utilized for the field control of *Sclerotium rolfsia.*

Harmful Activities of Fungi

A wide range of activities are harmful to humans. These are as follows:

1. ***Deterioration of articles*** Deterioration of leather, cellulose materials like paper and textiles, plastic, waxes, rubber, painted surfaces, wood, etc., is caused by *Aspergillus, Penicillum, Cladosporium, Alternaria, Rhizopus, Chaetomium, Aureobasidium,* etc.

2. ***Wood decay*** Some fungi cause white and brown rots. Cellulose is degraded in white rots and lignin in brown rots. Wood is mainly decomposed by *Polyporus tomentosus, P. pini, P. annosus, Fomes annosus* and *F. rimosus.*

3. ***Mycotoxins*** Some fungi produce mycotoxins which cause food poisoning. Mycotoxins are secondary fungal metabolites which when ingested by humans and animals cause intoxication termed mycotoxicosis. The toxin producing mould species include *Aspergillus, Penicillium* and *Fusarium.* Peanuts, cereals and oil seed crops are mainly contaminated by mycotoxins.

   According to the World Health Organization (1969), four groups of mycotoxins were considered to be causally associated with diseases in humans. These are:

   - Aflatoxins
   - Ochratoxins
   - Zearalenone
   - Trichothecenes

   Aflatoxin was first detected in the 1960s as a contaminant in groundnut. Fungi like *Aspergillus flavus, A. fumigatus, A. parasiticum* and *Penicillium islandicum* produce aflatoxins. They are the potential carcinogens which mainly cause liver cancer in man. They are heat-stable and they will survive most cooking conditions. Lactating animals ingesting aflatoxin contaminated feed excrete metabolites in the milk called aflatoxin M_1.

4. ***Plant disease*** Fungi are the causative agents of different diseases of the plants. These fungal diseases cause tremendous economic losses. About 30 thousand different diseases attack the economic plants grown for food or commercial purposes. The important diseases are:

   1. **Damping off** The seedlings of commercial crops like tomato, mustard, tobacco, peas, beans, corn and cotton are prone to this disease. It is caused by *Pythium* spp.

   2. **Apple scab** It is a serious disease of the apple crop.

   3. **Red rot of sugarcane** It is a serious disease of sugarcane which is caused by *Colletotrichum* spp.

   4. **Potato blight** Late blight of potato is caused by *Phytophthora infestans* and a heavy attack of this disease in Ireland in 1845 destroyed the entire potato crop and caused the

Irish famine. This led to the migration of Irish people to the US. Early blight of potato is caused by *Alternaria solani.*

5. **Downy mildew of grapes**   It ruins the vineyards and thus causes heavy losses to the crop. It is caused by *Peronospora* spp.

6. **Ergot of rye**   It is an important cereal disease which affects rye plants. It is caused by *Claviceps purpurea.*

7. **Rust disease**   They attack the cereal crops and forest timber. Some of them are black stem rust, yellow rust, and white rust.

8. **Black arm wilt and root rot of cotton**   These diseases are caused in the cotton plant which take a heavy toll of the crop every year.

9. **Smut diseases**   These are mainly caused in the inflorescence of cereals like corn, wheat, oats, etc.,which cause a serious reduction in the yield and quality of grain. It is caused by *Ustilago* spp.

10. **Wart disease of potato**   It is caused by *Synchytrium endobioticum* in potato plants.

11. **Club root of crucifers**   This disease is mainly noticed in crucifers and is caused by *Plasmodiophora brassicae.* It is a root pathogen.

12. **Tikka disease**   This disease is caused by *Cercosporra* spp. in the plants of groundnuts.

13. **Blast diseases of rice**   It is caused by *Pyricularia oryzae* in paddy.

5. *Disease of animals including humans*   Some human fungal diseases along with their causative organisms and the organs most commonly infected are given in the Table 1.1.

Table 1.1   Fungal disease in man

Disease	Causative organism	Organs infected
Athlete's foot	*Epidermophyton floccosum*	Foot
Blastomycosis	*Emmonsiella*	Lung
Cryptococcosis	*Cryptococcus neoformans*	Lung, central nervous system
Histoplasmosis	*Histoplasma capsulatum*	Reticuloendothelial tissue
Candidiasis	*Candida albicans*	Vaginal membranes in women and thrush in infants
Sporotrichosis	*Sporotrichum schenkii*	Subcutaneous tissue and lymphatic system
Ringworm	*Trichophyton myxotrichum*	Dead, keratinized tissue
Moniliasis	*Candida albicans*	Nails
Rhizosporidiosis	*Rhizosporidium sceberi*	Mucous membrane of nose, eye, lips, vagina and penis
Mucoramycosis	*Mucor rhizopus*	Lungs, central nervous system

FUNGAL BIOTECHNOLOGY

Biotechnology has been defined by Spinks (1980) as application of biological organisms, systems or processes to manufacturing industry. Fungal biotechnology is the application of fungi to manufacturing processes such as the production of pharmaceuticals, foodstuff and in fermentation. The use of yeast to produce alcoholic beverages, *Penicillium* to produce blue cheese, the cultivation of mushrooms and the use of the koji process to produce soysauce and other food products have been practised as commercial processes for hundreds of years. The development of industrial fermentation probably represents the beginning of modern biotechnology. Fungi can be used biotechnologically in various ways. For instance they can be used,

1.   to generate primary and secondary metabolites

2.   to produce enzymes

3.   as biomass

Some of the recent developments are,

1. *To grow aerobic fungi in submerged culture*   Stirred tank reactor for large-scale growth of aerobic microbes in submerged culture was developed. The modern tank reactor was developed for *Penicillium* fermentation.

2. *Fermenter design*   The rotating disc fermenter and the spouted bed fermenter have been designed for use with filamentous fungi. These are particularly suited to operation with immobilized cells. This technique is widely used for production of mushrooms, oriental foods such as tempeh biomass for use in animal feeds and for the production of organic acids and enzymes like diastase in certain Eastern countries.

3. *Genetics*   Principles of fungal biochemical genetics were applied to the production of improved strains of fungi in Penicillin production. Recent developments in protoplast fusion techniques could make the production of improved strains of *Penicillium* and *Aspergillus*. Genetic engineering had also its impact on fungal biotechnology. Successful techniques have been developed for cloning fungal genes in bacteria, using bacterial vectors. But only in the yeast, such strategies have been well-developed. In the yeast non-fungal genes could be cloned successfully. Yeasts are used as potential vehicles for the biosynthesis of complex macromolecules of medical importance. The protein, known as HBsAg is a surface antigen in the envelope of Hepatitis B virus which causes hepatitis in humans and chimpanzee. It is a valuable vaccine against the virus.

4. *Biosynthetic capabilities of fungi*   Fungi produce a wide variety of commercially important products which are the secondary metabolites. These are antibiotics (Penicillin, Cephalosporin, Griseofulvin) Ergot, Alkaloids, Gibberellic Acid and Mycotoxins.

5. *Fungal products*   These are the industrial products obtained from filamentous fungi. These include organic acids, pharmaceuticals, enzymes, insecticides, polysaccharides and biomass.

6. *Fungal biomass as food*   Fungal biomass in the form of baker's yeast which constitutes 2% by weight of bread and mushrooms are well-established as major food products.

7. *Fungal enzymes*   Fungi are well-known producers of industrial enzymes. These include amylases, amyloglucosidases, pectinases, proteinases, glucose oxidases and cellulases. Many fungi are able to degrade lignocellulose. These include *Fusarium, Paecilomyces, Chaetomium, Collybia, Coriolus* and *Poria.* Recently *Trichoderma* is shown to have a strong ability to degrade lignocellulose.

8. *Fungi as insecticides*   Fungi like *Metarhizium anisopliae* and *Verticillium lecanii* are used for the commercial production of some insecticides which are used against insects like corn borer, pine beetles and aphids.

9. *Oil to plastics*   Mutants of *Candida tropicalis* could carry out initial oxidation which convert hydrocarbons into dicarboxylic acid. These acids may then be used as starting materials for the manufacture of plastics and synthetic fibres.

10. *Fungal cell immobilization*   One recent innovation in fermentation technology is the use of cell immobilization technique. The controlled intentional attachment or aggregation of cells is called immobilization. Very high cell concentrations can be achieved by immobilization. This leads to increased productivity. This is applied in the case of cellulase production by *Trichoderma reesei* . The methods of cell immobilization include the attachment, entrapment, aggregation and containment. Aggregation has been exploited in beer production by yeast cells using tower fermenters. Ethanol is produced by using immobilized yeast cells.

2

DIVISION—MYXOMYCOTA

INTRODUCTION

The organisms included in this division Myxomycota are the cellular slime moulds, the true or plasmodial slime moulds and the net slime moulds. Their characteristic feature is the presence of a vegetative phase which may be an amoeba, an aggregation of amoebae (pseudoplasmodium) or a plasmodium. They differ from the true fungi in their phagotrophic nutrition, because their somatic parts consist only of protoplasts bounded by plasma membrane and are devoid of cell walls. Spores of the Myxomycota are, however, enveloped by a rigid cell wall similar to true fungi. They are useful experimental tools for cytologists, geneticists, morphogeneticists, molecular biologists and biochemists. Perhaps the greatest importance of these organisms to humans is their aesthetic value. They are the most beautiful entities to be found in the animal and plant kingdom. In most of the species, plasmodia act as scavengers and decomposers in nature.

It is doubtful the Myxomycota are closely related to the Eumycota. Perhaps they are more closely related to Protozoa. Various authors like Debary (1887), Lester (1925) and Hagelstein (1944) used the term Mycetozoa indicating their relationships with animals. Their view is shared by Olive (1870) who reviewed taxonomy of this group recently. However others like Shroetes (1897), Mac bride (1922) and Martin (1949) preferred to use the term Myxomycetes to indicate a possible link with the fungi. Recently Ainsworth (1973) classified them with the fungi.

KEY TO CLASSES OF MYXOMYCOTA

1. Assimilative phase free living amoebae which
   unite as a pseudoplasmodium before reproduction   Acrasiomycetes
   Assimilative phase a plasmodium.

2. Plasmodium forming networknet-plasmodium   Hydromyxomycetes
   Plasmodium not forming a network.

3.   Plasmodium saprophytic, free living   Myxomycetes

Plasmodium parasitic within cells of the host plant   Plasmodiophoromycetes

Class—Acrasiomycetes

They are commonly called cellular slime moulds. Their characteristic features are the following.

1.   The vegetative phase is naked, amochoid cells or myxamochae (minute plasmodia in some).
2.   Nutrition is by ingestion of bacteria or other food particles.
3.   Amoebae aggregate to form a slug or pseudoplasmodium from which the fruit body develops.
4.   Fructifications are sporocarps (slender tubular stalk bearing one or few spores) as in protostelium or sporocarps (multicellular fruit structures in which sorus of spores is borne at the tip of a single-celled or multicellular stalk) as in *Dictyostelium*.

Class—Hydromyxomycetes

These are commonly called net slime moulds. In this class, thallus exists as uninucleate spindle cells with extensive filaments. These cells form a network of branched tubes—net plasmodium or filoplasmodium. Labyrinthula is the most common form which is parasitic on marine algae. Reproduction is by congregation, cyst formation and zoospore formation.

Class—Myxomycetes

These are called true slime moulds. Their main characteristic features are:

1.   They are common on moist, decaying wood and other substrates.
2.   Assimilative stage is a free-living plasmodium.
3.   Nutrition is by ingestion of bacteria, fungal cells, etc.
4.   Reproduction is by spores; under favourable conditions, plasmodium gives rise to sporophores.
5.   Asexual reproduction is by binary fission of myxamoebae or fragmentation of plasmodium.
6.   Sexual reproduction is by fusion of myxamoebae or zoospores to form zygotes from which plasmodia develop.

3

Class—Plasmodiophoromycetes

INTRODUCTION

The chief characteristic features

1. Microscopic, obligate parasites (biotrophs of fresh-water algae), fungi and angiosperms (usually in the roots).
2. Thallus is a naked holocarpic plasmodium.
3. Except for the reinfection phases (in soil water), the life cycle occurs entirely within the host.
4. Zoospores are biflagellate and anisokont, i.e., with a short anterior and a long posterior flagellum (flagella of unequal length); both of whiplash type.

Genus—*Plasmodiophora*

The best known species is *Plasmodiophora brassicae*, the causal organism of "club-root" or "finger and toe" disease of crucifers, particularly the brassicas. The disease is known throughout the world and mainly occurs in temperate climate. Records of this disease go back as far as the 13th century in Western Europe. It became so destructive on cabbage in the vegetable gardens of St. Petersburg in Russia in 1872, that the Royal Russian Gardening Society had to offer a prize to anybody who could find its cause and method of control. Woronin, a Russian plant pathologist, did classical work on the nature of this disease and his first report came out in 1874. The disease is common in acidic and poorly drained soil.

The disease progresses to a considerable extent before signs of it are visible above the ground. When plants are attacked at the seedling stage, they can be killed. The most obvious and characteristic symptoms appear on the roots and sometimes on the underground parts of the stem. The symptoms consist of small or large spindle-shaped, spherical or club-shaped swellings on the roots and rootlets

(Figure 3.1). The root hairs are commonly hypertrophied and expand at their tips to form club-shaped swellings. The swollen roots contain large number of spherical, small, resting spores, and on decay these spores are released into the soil.

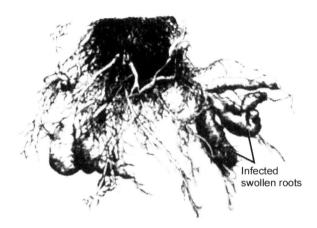

Infected
swollen roots

Figure 3.1   Cabbage roots infected by *Plasmodiophora brassicae*—the cause of club-root disease

Cook and Swartz (1939) showed that the life cycle of *P.brassicae* comprises two distinct phases, the haplophase (primary phase) and the diplophase (secondary phase). The former occurs in the root hairs and the latter in the cells of the main root cortex of the susceptible host plant. Each phase includes a number of successive stages (Figure 3.2 a–p).

Primary phase   The resting spores or sporangia (cysts) which are differentiated by meiosis (form the diploid protoplast of the sporothallus) are pioneer structures of the haplophase which occurs in the root hairs.

The resting spore or sporangium is a tiny hyaline, spherical, uninucleate, haploid structure up to 4.0 μm in diameter. The sporangial wall is differentiated into three layers but in many cases it showed only two layers. The outer layer is thick, granular and has surface spinules. The cytoplasm shows the presence of organelles such as mitochondria, endoplasmic reticulum, dictyosomes, a single nucleus and many ribosomes. Numerous lipid globules of various sizes are present in the cytoplasm. The mature spores are released into the soil when the clubs undergo decay. The resting spore initiates the life cycle.

The resting spores may germinate immediately or remain dormant in the soil for several years. The spore germinates in a favourable condition. It absorbs water and swells. The uninucleate protoplasm emerges as a single zoospore which is spherical or pear-shaped. This primary zoospore is biflagellated with two flagella of unequal length, both of whiplash type and the usual 9+2 arrangement of fibrils. Each zoospore has a short anterior and a long posterior flagellum. The zoospore swims in a film of water in the soil or creeps over soil particles like an amoeba. On contact with the root hair of a suitable host, the zoospore becomes attached and amoeboid. At

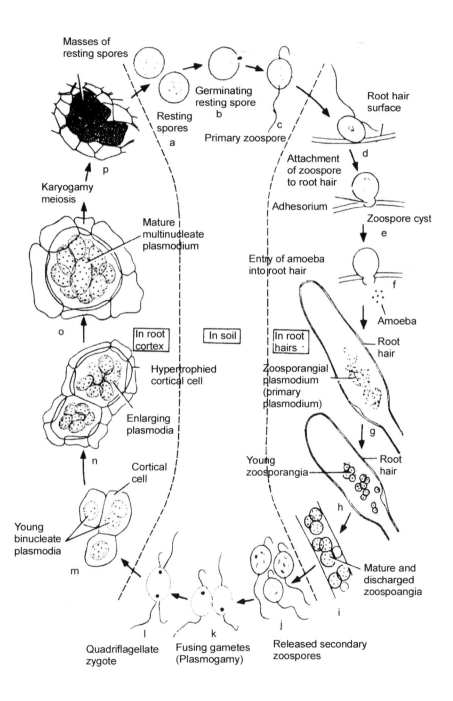

Figure 3.2 (a–p) Different stages in the life cycle of *Plasmodiophora brassicae*

this stage it is called myxamoeba. The myxamoeba retracts its flagella and enters the root hair directly by a partial dissolution of the root hair wall. There is rapid injection of the myxamoeba into the root hairs of the host. The cyclosis of host cytoplasm sweeps the myxamoeba away from the penetration site soon after injection.

Primary plasmodium (Gametothallus)   The uninucleate myxamoeba enlarges to form a thallus in the root hair. The protoplasm increases in size and the haploid nucleus divides repeatedly. The small, naked, multinucleated acellular mass of protoplasm constituting the thallus is called the primary plasmodium. It is a haploid structure and is called the gametothallus.

Sexual reproduction   The haploid primary plasmodium is concerned with sexual reproduction. The cytoplasm of the gametothallus in the root hair cleaves into many uninucleate daughter protoplasts. Each daughter protoplast secretes a membrane around it and functions as a gametangium. The gametangia are small, spherical, thin-walled, uninucleate structures. The haploid nucleus of the gametangium undergoes mitosis to form four to eight daughter nuclei. Cytoplasm aggregates around each nucleus and it develops into a spindle-shaped, biflagellate isogamete which is smaller than the zoospores. The tiny gametangial wall bursts and the gametes are liberated into the root hairs of the host or outside the host tissue by the disintegration of the host tissue. After liberation, the isogametes fuse in pairs to form a diploid flagellate zygote. It is not definitely known whether the gametes fuse in the root hairs or in the cortical cells after migration. Karyogamy does not follow plasmogamy. If fusion occurs outside the host, the quadriflagellate zygote reinfects the root.

Secondary phase   The secondary phase starts with the quadriflagellate zygote. It may be formed inside the root hair or outside the root hair. It reinfects the host and enters the root cortex to form binucleate plasmodia. It is not known whether there is active penetration of cell wall or whether plasmodia are transferred passively from cell to cell. Within the invaded cell the myxamoeba by subsequent growth accompanied by repeated karyokinesis (mitosis) of its diploid nucleus (but no cytokinesis) grows to form a large naked multinucleate plasmodium. In the mature stage it may occupy the entire lumen of the infected host cell and it lies immersed in the cytoplasm.

The presence of the secondary plasmodia in the cortical host cells brings about many metabolic responses in the infected cells. This is termed hypertrophy. Besides hypertrophy, the infected cells show excessive multiplication and this is called hyperplasia. This stimulates the neighbouring cell of the host to divide and redivide. Consequently there is excessive proliferation of infected host cells in the form of swellings on the diseased roots. These are called the clubs or galls. The infected roots act as sinks for growth materials produced in the aerial parts. The rapid growth of clubs prevents the development of cork cambium at the root surface. Then it brings about decay of clubs and results in permanent wilting or retarded growth.

Akaryotic stage   The diploid secondary plasmodium fills the entire lumen of the hypertrophied cortical cells. It ceases to grow in size. With this a new phase sets in. During this phase, the diploid nuclei of the plasmodium seem to lose their content and disappear. The chromatin fails to take the usual stain and is called the akaryotic stage.

Formation of resting spores The nuclei in the plasmodium reappear and the protoplasmic mass of the plasmodium cleaves around each nucleus. The entire plasmodium is thus transformed into a large number of tiny, uninucleate, spherical bodies. Each is surrounded by a wall of its own and is called as resting spore.

Nuclear behaviour The nature of the akaryotic stage was an enigma. Lutman (1913) suggested that meiosis takes place during the formation of resting spores. Milovidon (1931) claimed that the akaryotic stage represents the meiotic prophase I. Thus the akaryotic stage represents the transition between the vegetative plasmodium and the dormant phase represented by the resting spores which are haploid structures. Prior to resting spore formation the diploid nucleus undergoes meiosis. Thus the resting spores are haploid.

The resting spores are released into the soil as the roots undergo decay and decomposition by soft rot organisms. The cell wall of the resting spore contains chitin, a cell wall material. The chitinous nature of the sporangial wall enables them to withstand adverse conditions. The resting spores or cysts perennate in the soil. They germinate to produce zoospores on the onset of suitable conditions to continue the life cycle.

Control measures The use of resistant varieties and long rotation are effective control measures. Fungicidal transplanting liquids are employed. The use of pentachloronitrobenzene or mercuric or mercurous chloride in the transplanting liquid is effective in checking infection. Use of soil that is from the pathogen in the transplantation of seedlings is a useful preventive measure.

Alternation of generation There is distinct alternation of generations in the life cycle of *Plasmodiophora brassicae*. The resting spores, the zoospores, the haploid primary plasmodium, the gametangia and isogametes represent the gametophyte or haplophase. The zygote and the secondary plasmodium represent the sporophyte or diplophase. Meiosis occurs prior to the formation of zoospores (Figure 3.3).

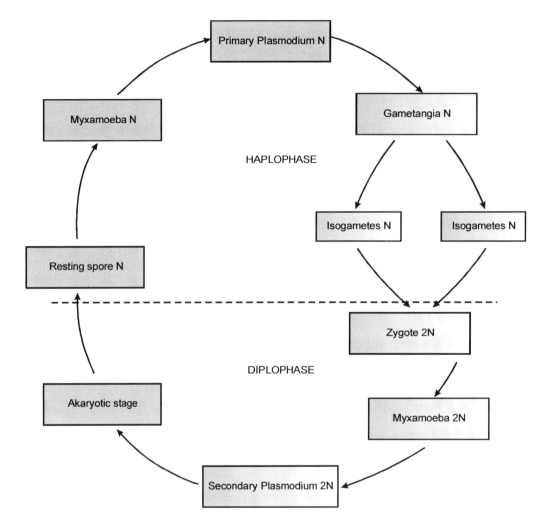

Figure 3.3 Life cycle of *Plasmodiophora brassicae*

4

CLASS—CHYTRIDIOMYCETES

Subdivision Mastigomycotina (zoosporic fungi) Fungi which produce motile zoospores are placed under the subdivision Mastigomycotina. The zoospores are uniflagellate or biflagellate. The flagellum may be of whiplash or tinsel type. The anterior or posterior position of the flagella may be known by their orientation during locomotion. A characteristic feature of the biflagellate spores is that during movement, the flagella are always oppositely directed. On the basis of number (one or two), position (anterior, posterior or lateral) and type (whiplash and tinsel) of the flagella on the zoospores, the subdivision Mastigomycotina is divided into three classes.

Key to classes of Mastigomycotina

1. Zoospores uniflagellate.

   Flagellum posterior,

   whiplash type—Chytridiomycetes

   Flagellum anterior, tinsel type—Hyphochytridiomycetes

2. Zoospores, biflagellate

   Flagella equal, posterior

   flagellum whiplash-type;

   anterior tinsel-type;

   cell wall cellulosic—Oomycetes

   Flagella of unequal size, both whiplash; thallus always plasmodial—Plasmodiophoromycetes

DISTINGUISHING FEATURES OF CLASS—CHYTRIDIOMYCETES

1. Vegetative state typically unicellular or short chain of cells attached to the substratum by rhizoids. A few forms have undeveloped hyphae.

2. Cell wall is made up of chitin and glucans.

3. Parent thallus is normally haploid except unusual in Allomyces.

4. Asexual reproduction by posteriorly uniflagellate zoospores; flagellum of whiplash type; zoospores formed by cleavage of cytoplasm in a sporangium.

5. Sexual reproduction by motile gametes released from gametangia which fuse to form a diploid zygote that functions as a resting stage and then undergoes meiosis to form a new haploid thallus.

ORDER—CHYTRIDIALES

Members of Chytridiales are referred to as chytrids. They live as parasites or saprophytes in water and soil. They grow internally in algae and watermoulds. The thallus is holocarpic or eucarpic. Cell wall is formed of chitin or chitin and cellulose. The thallus is epibiotic or endobiotic monocentric or polycentric.

Zoosporangia are spherical or pear-shaped, inoperculate or operculate. Zoospores are posteriorly uniflagellate, flagellum is of whiplash type. Sexual reproduction is unknown in many forms. Whenever present, the zygote becomes transformed into a resting spore which upon germination produces zoospores.

Sparrow (1960, 1973) has divided Chytridiales into nine families, on the basis of their zoospore liberation. The nine families are

> i. Olpidiaceae
> ii. Achylogetonaceae
> iii. Synchytriaceae
> iv. Phlyctidiaceae
> v. Rhizidiaceae
> vi. Cladochytriaceae
> vii. Physodermataceae
> viii. Chytriaceae
> ix. Megachytriaceae

Synchytriaceae

Thallus is holocarpic and endobiotic which at the time of reproduction becomes converted into a group of sporangia (sorus) or into a prosorus which later gives rise to a sorus of sporangia. Zoospores are typically of chytrid type. Sexual reproduction is by copulation of isogametes resulting in the formation of thick-walled resting sporangia.

Genus—Synchytrium

Synchytrium is the largest genus which induces galls on vascular plants. Karling (1964) recognized 6 subgenera and 200 species. These are parasitic on vascular plants, mosses, ferns and aquatic alage. They cause formation of galls on leaves, stems and fruits.

The most serious parasite is *S. endobioticum*, the cause of black wart disease of potato. From India this species has been reported in potato plants mostly from Darjeeling district of West Bengal and adjoining areas of Nepal. The fungus cannot survive in hot areas.

Sychytrium endobioticum is a soil borne fungal parasite causing the wart disease of potato in hilly areas with cool and moist climate. Diseased potato tubers bear dark brown, warty, cauliflower-like excrescences. Galls may also be formed on aerial part. The dark warts on the tubers are galls in which the host cells, have been stimulated to divide by the presence of the fungus (Figure 4.1(a–b)).

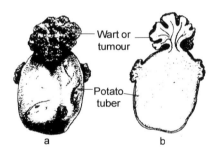

Figure 4.1 (a–b)   Potato Black Wart disease caused by *Synchytrium endobioticum*

Thallus   The thallus is holocarpic and a spherical sac surrounded by a wall. The zoospores which are released from infected tissues of the host swim actively for about 2–3 hours in the film of soil water. When they are in contact with host, the naked uniflagellate zoospores come to rest and withdraw their flagella. It enters the host cell through a pore, dissolved by their enzyme activity. The naked (wall less) unicellular thallus of the fungus grows in size at the expense of the food absorbed from the host cell. The infected cell enlarges and becomes pear-shaped. The cells around it are stimulated to uncontrolled division and growth (hyperplasia and hypertrophy) which ultimately gives rise to the warty outgrowths. The walls of these cells adjacent to the infected cell are thickened and assume a dark brown colour. The infected cell eventually dies and the parasite passes to the bottom of the host cell, enlarges, becomes spherical and fills the lower part of the host cell. A double-layered chitinous wall of golden brown colour is secreted around the thallus and at this stage the thallus is termed as prosorus. The thallus remains uninucleate and the nucleus enlarges and attains a size which is probably the largest among fungi (up to 80 μm in diameter).

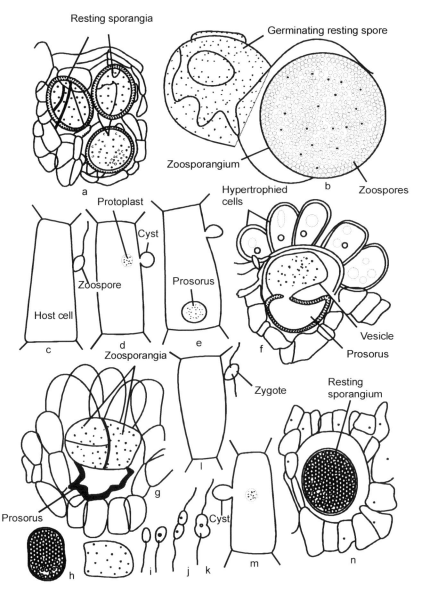

Figure 4.2 (a–n) Stages in the life cycle of *Synchytrium endobioticum*. a—Resting sporangia in section of wart, b—A germinating resting sporangium to show the formation of vesicle containing a single globose sporangium. (c–e)—Infection stages by a zoospore, f—Section of infected host cells containing a prosorus which extrudes a vesicle. Infected cells become hypertrophied. g—Cleavage of vesicle contents into zoosporangia. h—Two extruded zoosporangia. i—Zoospores, (j–k)—Fusion of isogametes to form zygotes. l—Attachment of zygote to host cell surface. l, m—Infection of host cell, the protophast of parasite introduced into host cell. n—Young resting sporangium formed from infection by a zygote.

Asexual phase The prosorus now germinates and the inner wall of the prosorus protrudes out through a pore in the outer wall and then expands as a vesicle which enlarges upwards and fills the upper half of the host cell. The contents of the prosorus including the nucleus are transferred to the vesicle. The nucleus generally divides mitotically and the vesicle contains about 32 nuclei. Cytoplasmia contents of the vesicle become cleaved into a number of sporangia. Thus a sorus of 4–9 sporangia develop. Each sporangium by further nuclear divisions comes to have about 200–300 nuclei. Finally each nucleus with the surrounding cytoplasm is differentiated into a zoospore. When the zoospores are mature the sporangia absorb water and swell. This causes the host cell containing the sporangia to burst open. The zoospores are released through a small slit in the sporangial wall. There may be 500–600 zoospores in a large sporangium. Zoospores swim actively in the water film for sometime. They infect the potato tubers in the same way as do the zoospores produced by the resting sporangia. This continues throughout the crop season and several successive generations of zoospores are produced which cause repeated infections resulting in severe infection.

Sexual phase Resting sporangia are formed as a result of sexual reproduction. With the arrival of dry weather, the zoospores behave as gametes and undergo fusion to bring about sexual reproduction. The gametes are smaller in size than the zoospores. The gametes are similar in size and shape, i.e., copulation is isogamous. According to Curtis, zoospores form a single sporangium may not fuse and therefore, show physiological heterothallism. Probably zoospores which act as male gametes swim actively and the female gametes become quiescent and probably secrete a hormone sirenin which attracts male gametes towards them chemotactically, sexual fusion takes place and the biflagellate zygote cell, after a period of swimming infects tubers essentially like the zoospores. Karyogamy occurs in the young zygote before penetration and therefore, the fungal thallus that grows in the epidermal cell is diploid. It induces hyperplasia in the adjoining cells and ultimately the infected cell lies buried deep in the mass of wart cells. The diploid fungus cell which lies at the bottom of the infected host cell, grows, develops a thick two-layered wall and transforms into a resting spore. The outer wall is pigmented (dark brown) and forms ridges or folds which appear as spines in section. Due to the decay of the tubers, the resting speres are released into the soil. Presumably, the zygote and the young resting sporangia are diploid and meiosis occurs during germination of resting sporangia prior to zoospore formation. The resting spores germinate after about 2 months of dormancy when that host is available ; otherwise they are capable of long survival (Figure 4.2). An outline of the life cycle of *S. endobioticum* is shown in Figure 4.4.

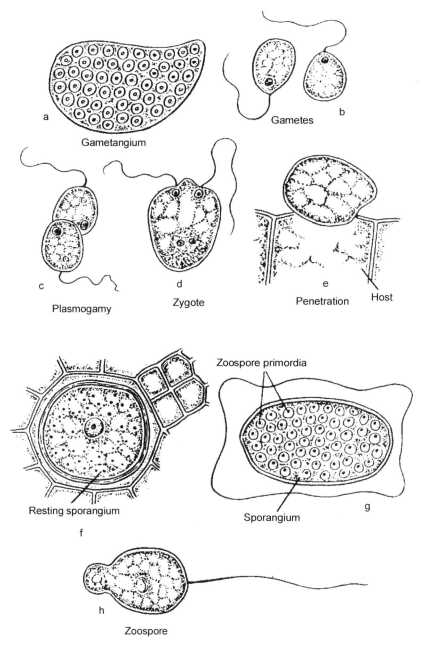

Figure 4.3 (a–h)   *Synchytrium endobioticum.* Sexual phase of the life cycle. a—Gametangium; b—Two gametes released from the gametangium; c—Fusing gametes; d—zygote; e—Zygote penetrating the host epidermal cell; f—Resting sporangium; g—Germinating resting sporangium with zoospore primordia; h—Released zoospore

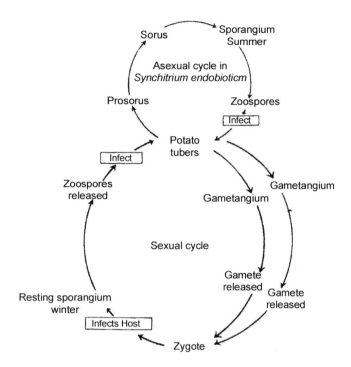

Figure 4.4 Word diagram of the life cycle of *Synchytrium endobioticum*

Control of black wart Quarantine regulations are practised to reduce the spread of the pathogen. In India the entry to potatoes from Darjeeling Hills where wart disease is known to occur, has been prohibited. Many disease-resistant varieties have been produced in recent years. The application of lime and use of fungicides in the soil before planting have given some useful results.

ORDER—BLASTOCLADIALES

They are mostly saprophytes in soil, water, mud or colonizing plant and animal debris. The thallus is eucarpic, monocentric or polycentric. Asexual reproduction is by posteriorly uniflagellate zoospore with whiplash type of flagellum. Sexual reproduction is by planogametic copulation of similar gamates. A number of distinct life history patterns are found in the group. Sparrow (1960, 1973) recognized three families

1. Coclommycetaceae
2. Catenoriaceae
3. Blastocladiaceae

Genus—*Allomyces*

Allomyces is the most extensively studied genus in the family Blastocladiaceae.

Species of *Allomyces* are most frequent in mud or soil of tropical countries. It is commonly found in places which are periodically wetted and dried, in rice fields, ponds and sluggish rivers. From India, the genus was first reported by Butler (1911). *Allomyces arbusculus* is the most common species. It is easy to cultivate this by baiting technique. Soil samples are placed in water to which baits of boiled hemp seeds are added. Baits become colonized by zoopores. From these crude culture, zoospores may be pipetted out on suitable agar media.

Thallus The thallus is eucarpic, differentiated into a trunklike portion bearing rhizoids below. It is branched dichotomously above with sporangia of various kinds at the tips of branches. The hyphae are pseudoseptate and the pseudosepta are incomplete and wheel-like with radiating strands. Cell wall is composed of chitin with appreciable quantities of glucan, ash and protein. Emerson (1941) on the basis of his studies of extensive collections obtained from all over the world, divided *Allomyces* into three sub genera: *Euallomyces*, *Cystogenes* and *Brachyallomyces* which differ drastically from each other.

Euallomyces shows isomorphic alternation of generations, while *Cystogenes* shows a heteromorphic alternation of generation having a reduced gametophyte in the form of a tiny cyst. *Brachyallomyces* lacks the gametothallus and, thus, has no alternation of generation.

Subgenus: *Euallomyces*—Long-cycled

Allomyces arbuscula, *A. macerogynous* and *A. javanicus* are placed under the subgenus *Euallomyces*. In these species there are two types of thalli such as the asexual or sporothalli and the sexual or gametothalli.

Sporothalli or asexual plants—They are diploid and bear two types of sporangia, the thin-walled mitosporangia producing mitospores and thick-walled resting sporangia or meiosporangia producing meiospores. Both the types of sporangia are borne on the same thallus singly or in chains at the tips of branches.

1. *Mitosporangia* They are thin-walled, papillate zoosporangia formed singly or in rows at the tips of the branches. The nuclei of the sporangia undergo mitosis and the cytoplasmic contents become cleaved around the nuclei to form diploid colourless zoospores, the mitospores. The mitospores are released from mitosporangia and they swim for a brief period, encyst and germinate to form a new generation of diploid sporothalli.

2. *Meiosporangia* These zoosporangia are dark-brown, thick-walled and pitted, formed at the tips of branches. The nuclei in the meiosporangia undergo meriosis and thus results in the formation of haploid meiospores. The outer wall cracks open by a slit and the inner wall balloons outwards, then open by one or more pores to release the zoospores. The zoospores are mobile and posteriorly uniflagellated. The haploid zoospores are slightly smaller than the diploid zoospores but structurally both are identical. The meiospores swim for sometime, come to rest and germinate to form the thalli with characteristic trunk-like portion bearing dichotomous branches. These haploid zoospores, on germination, give rise to gametothalli.

Gametothalli or sexual plants The gametophytes on maturity forms both male and female gametangia on the same thallus. Thus, the thallus is monoecious. The gametangia lie one above the

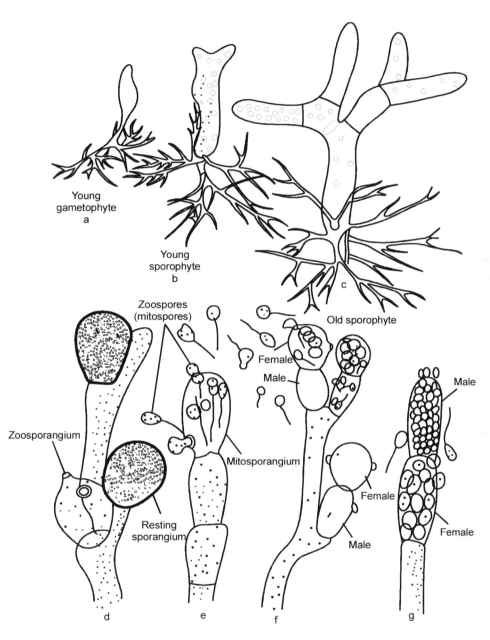

Figure 4.5 (a–g) Stages in the life cycles of *Allomyces arbusculus* (a–f) and *A. macrogynus* (g) showing *Euallomyces* pattern. a—Young gametophyte, b—Young sporophyte, c—Old sporophyte, d—A part of mature sporophyte bearing resting sporangia (meisporangia) and zoosporangia (mitosporangia), e—Release of mitospores form mitosporangium, f—A part of mature gametophyte of *A. arbusculus* bearing gametangia at tips of hyphal brances, g—A branch tip of gametophyte of *A. macrogynus*

other. In *A. arbuscula*, the female gemetangium lies above the male gametangium and in *A. macrogynous*, the male gametangium lies over the female gametangium The male gametangia are smaller and orange-coloured due to presence of r-carotene while the female gametangia are bigger and colourless. The gametangia bear a number of colourless papillae on their walls which eventually dissolve to form pores. The gametangial contents are cleaved into uninucleate gametes which differ in size and pigmentation. The male gametangium releases smaller, more active orange-coloured male gametes. Both the gametes are posterorly uniflagellated. After swimming for sometime, the gametes then pair off. A hormone called sirenin, is produced by the female gametes (Machlis, 1958) which exerts a chemotactic influence on the male gametes. When the male gametes fuse with the female gamete, karyogamy follows and a biflagellate diploid zygote is produced. The diploid zygote comes to rest, sheds the flagella, becomes round and encysts. It produces a germ tube which develops into rhizoids. The cyst elongates, divides dichotomously and develops into a diploid thallus or asexual plants (Figure 4.5 a–g).

Sub-genus: Cystogenes   *Allomyces moniliformis* and *A. neomoniliformis* (*A. cystogenus*) are placed under the subgenus *Cystogenes*. Here the gametophytic generation is suppressed. It is not represented by independent sexual plants but only by a cyst. The asexual plants resemble those of *Euallomyces* bearing both mitosporangia and brown thick-walled punctate meiosporangia. The thin-walled mistosporangia bear a single terminal papilla.The zoospores from these sporangia germinate to form asexual plants. The behaviour of meiosporangia is however, different. The thin sporangial wall breaks open irregularly and the sporangium slips out. It germinates very soon. Before germinations it assumes a spherical shape and its outer wall cracks. The contents of the resting sporangium divide to form up to 30 amoeboid bodies which escape through the pores. Meiosis occurs in the resting sporangia. These bodies are sluggish and these encyst quickly. Contents of each haploid cyst divide to form four colourless posteriorly uniflagellate swarmers which escape through a single papilla on the cyst wall. These swarmers behave as isogametes and copulate to form biflagellate zygotes. The zygote swims for sometime, comes to rest and develops into an asexual plant. Thus in Cystogenes, there is a diploid asexual generation, and the haploid phase is represented by the cyst and gametes. Thus the life cycle shows a heteromorphic alternation of generation where the gametothallus and the sporothallus are not identical (Figure 4.6 a–h).

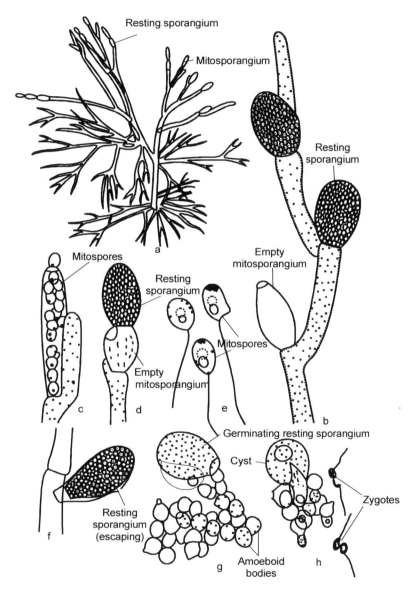

Figure 4.6 (a–h) Stages in the life cycle of *Allomyces neomoniliformis*, showing *Cystogenes* pattern. a—Asexual plant bearing resting sporangia and zoosporangia (mitosporangia), b—Branch tips of asexual plant magnified, c—A mitosporangium releasing mitospores, d—Branch tip showing a terminal resting sporangium and sub-terminal empty zoosporangium (mitosporangium). e—Mitospores. f—Resting sporangium escaping from its surrounding envelope, g—Germinating resting sporangium. A thin-walled vesicle has ballooned out through the crack wall. The swarmers that escaped from the vesicle have become encysted into amoeboid bodies immediately. h—Germination of a cyst to release swarmers. Released swarmers pair to form zygotes.

Subgenus: *Brachyallomyces*   The typical example of this subgenus is *Allomyces anomalus* and it is characterised by lack of alternation of generations. They have neither sexual plants nor cysts in their life cycle. There are only asexual plants which bear mitosporangia and resting sporangia. The spores from the resting sporangia develop into asexual plants directly. Meiosis does not occur and the zoospores produced by the resting sporangia are diploid. The zoospores on germination give rise to diploid asexual plants.

(The three types of life cycle are represented in Figure 4.7)

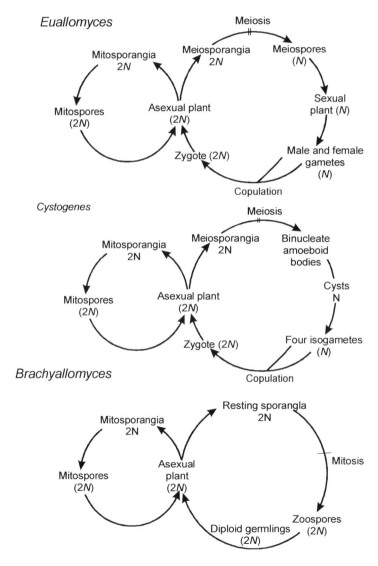

Figure 4.7   Diagrammatic outlines of the life cycle patterns of *Allomyces*

5

CLASS—OOMYCETES

INTRODUCTION

Oomycetes are characterized by

1. laterally biflagellate reniform zoospore
2. presence of cellulose in the cell wall, and
3. the thick-walled zoospore formed as a result of sexual reproduction.

In the biflagellate zoospores, the two flagella are laterally attached and are dissimilar in structure and size. One is 'tinsel' and the other of 'whiplash' type. Sexual reproduction is by oogamy which involves a club-shaped antheridium and a more or less globose oogonium containing one or more non-motile female gamete called the oosphere or egg.

The class Oomycetes has been divided by Sparrow (1973) into four orders such as

- Saprolegniales
- Leptomitales
- Lagenidiales and
- Peronosporales.

Order—Saprolegniales

Saprolegniales are called the water moulds. Most of these fungi are aquatic saprophytes and some are soil inhabitants. They are abundant in wet soils, lakes and fresh waters. Most of them thrive best in fresh water. The thallus is holocarpic or eucarpic.

Asexual reproduction is by biflagellate zoospores and the zoospores are dimorphic. Sexual reproductions is oogamous with a large spherical oogonium containing one to many eggs. Plasmogamy is by gametangial contact, only one nucleus is introduced into each egg.

Genus—Saprolegnia   Species of *Saprolegnia* are common in fresh water and soil, most of which are saprophytic on plant and animal remains. However, species such as *S. parasitica* cause diseases of fish and their eggs. The species may be easily grown by baiting technique. Baits such as seeds of hemp, poppy or corn, dead ants and insects are used. If seeds are used, they are sterilized by boiling, split and crushed. The bait is placed in pond water or the soil solution from which these fungi are to be isoloated. In a few days hyphae appear on the seeds which may be removed and grown in pure culture on liquid media. Autoclaved tap water alone or mixed with pond water is a highly suitable medium for growth.

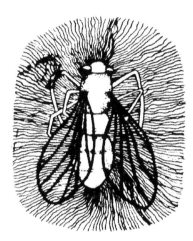

Figure 5.1   *Saprolegnia* sp. growing on a dead insect in water

Reproduction   The thallus is a mycelium and it is coenocytic, branched. The hyphae are fairly wide and stout. It is composed of two kinds of hyphae such as rhizoidal hyphae and extramatrical hyphae. The rhizoidal hyphae are short hyphae which penetrate the substratum. They anchor the mycelium and absorb nutrition. The extramatrical hyphae are long hyphae which grow out from the surface of the substratum into water. These hyphae are long, slender and extensively branched. They are aseptate and coenocytic. Septa, however, appear in connection with the formation of reproductive organs and rarely in older hyphae (Figure 5.1).

Thallus   After a certain period of growth and under suitable conditions *Saprolegnia* enters the reproduction phase.

Asexual reproduction   It takes place by vegetative methods and sporulation.

Vegetative reproduciton   It takes place by the following methods.

i. Fragmentation

The old hyphae break up into pieces of variable lengths and these fragments develop into new mycelia.

ii. Formation of gemmae

Gemmae are thick-walled, enlarged, terminal or intercalary portions of hyphae. These portions are packed with dense cytoplasm and are cut off from the rest of the mycelium by the septa. These may occur singly or in chains and are of various shapes. These are also known as chlamydospores. They remain viable for long periods. Mostly they germinate by germ tube to form new mycelium.

iii. Zoospores

This is the most common method of asexual reproduction. Zoospores are formed within the sporangia which develop terminally on the hyphae. The hyphal tips swell and become club-shaped. Dense cytoplasm with many nuclei then accumulates around the central vacuole of hyphal tips. A septum develops at the base of the sporangium. This is called zoosporangium. The contents of the zoosporangium become cleaved into uninucleate pieces, each of which differentiates into a zoospore. Zoospores are pear-shaped with two apical flagella.

A characteristic feature of *Saprolegnia* is that following the discharge of the zoosporangium, growth is renewed from the septum at its base, so that a new apex develops inside that wall of old sporangium. This in turn, may develop into a zoosporangium discharging its spores through the old pore. This phenomenon is known as proliferation of zoosporangium. Proliferation of zoosporangium is defined as the successive production of sporangia within the older sporangia. Thus several zoosporangial walls may be found inside each other.

The pear-shaped zoospores are apically biflagellate and are called primary zoospores. They swim for sometime, come to rest, withdraw their flagella and encyst to form a primary cyst. After a period of rest of 20–30 hours the cyst germinates to release another kind of zoospore, which is bean-shaped with two lateral flagellae. These zoospores are called secondary zoospores. This phenomenon of occurrence of two distinct motile stages in the asexual reproduction is known as displanetism. In some cases there may be phenomenon of polyplanetism or repeated emergence. The secondary zoospore swims for some time and encyst to form secondary cysts. These cysts then germinate by germ tube to form new mycelium.

Sexual reproduction It is oogamous and takes place by gametangial contact The sex organs are called antheridia and oogonia. Majority of the species are homothallic and monoecious. The hyphae are self-fertile, i.e., hyphae developed from a single zoospore form oogonia and antheridia. Both antheridia and oogonia develop on same hyphal branch. The oogonia develop first on the main or lateral branches. They are mostly terminal and occur singly or in chains. Oogonia are spherical, oval or pyriform and cut off by aseptum from main hypha. Sometimes the oogonia are intercalary in position. The mutinucleate protoplasm inside the oogonium is uniformly granular, but soon becomes cleaved into 5 to 10 round oospheres or eggs. In the beginning the eggs are multinucleate, but later, all but one nuclei degenerate in each egg. The entire protoplasm of oogonium is used up in the formation of oospheres. Thus it has no periplasm.

The male sex organ or the antheridium is borne on long or short slender hyphae called the antheridiophores. These may arise from the same hyphal branch which bears the oogonium and immediately below it or from a different hyphae. In the first case, the antheridia are said to be androgynous or monoclinous and in the latter diclinous. Antheridia are elongated, tubular, or club-shaped multinucleated structures delimited by a basal cross wall. It contains abundant protoplasm.

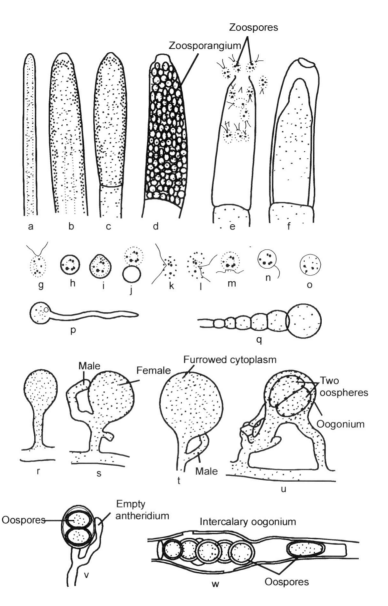

Figure 5.2 (a–w) Stages in the life cycle of *Saprolegnia*. a—Apex of vegetative hypha, (b–d)—Stages in the development of zoosporangium, e—Release of zoospores f—Proliferation of zoosporangium, g—Primary zoospore (first motile stage), h—Primary cyst, (i, j)—Germination of primary cyst to release secondary zoospore (second motile stage), (k–m)—Secondary zoospores, (n,o)—Secondary cysts, p—Germinating secondary cyst, q—Chain of gemmae, (r–u)—stages in development of oogonium, v—Oogoonium with two mature oospores, w—Intercalary oogonium lacking antheridia. The oospores have developed apogamously.

Fertilization   At maturity the antheridiophore grows towards the oogonium till the antheridium becomes closely attached to it. One or more antheridia may develop around each oogonium. A fine tubular outgrowth arises from the antheridium at the point of contact which is called the fertilizaton tube. It pierces the oogonial wall and may give out slender branches. Each branch makes its way to one of the oospheres within the oogonium. One male nucleus is discharged into each egg. Karyogamy takes place. The zygote or the fertilized egg secretes a thick wall to form the oospore. Usually many oospores are found in an oogonium. The zoospore is gorged with reserve food materials and it is a resting structure (Figure 5.2).

Germination of oospore   Mature oospores are liberated by the degeneration of the oogonial wall. During favourable conditions the oospore germinates to form a germ tube. The diploid nucleus undergoes mitosis at the time of germination. The germ tube may directly grow into a mycelium. Sometimes it swells to form a germ sporangium. The protoplasmic contents of the germ sporangium produces biflagellate zoospores. Each zoospore germinates to form a new mycelium.

Oospheres which fail to be fertilized develop parthenorganically into parthenospores. The parthenospore is apparently similar to an oospore and this develops into a new mycelium, parthenogenitically.

Life cycle of Saprolegnia   The life cycle of *Saprolegnia* is diplontic with no alternation of generations. The thallus is diploid and meiosis occurs in the gametangia during the formation of gamete. Gametes represent the only haploid phase in the life cycle (Figure 5.3).

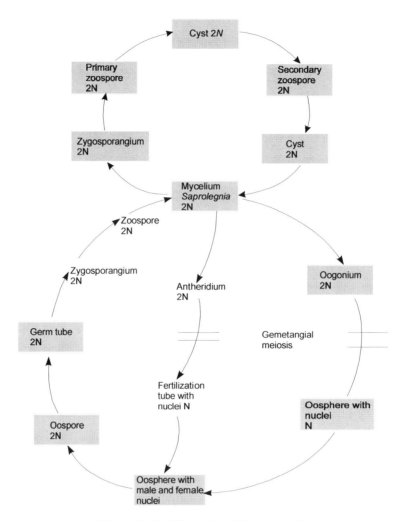

Figure 5.3 Life cycle of Saprolegnia

6

CLASS—PERONOSPORALES

GENERAL CHARACTERISTICS

In habit they range from aquatic to terrestrial ones. Most of the terrestrial species are plant parasites which cause serious diseases of important crop plants. The mycelium is aseptate, coenocytic and the hyphae are intracellular or intercellular. Asexual reproduction takes place by the formation of motile or non-motile asexual spores produced within sporangia They are developed either on somatic hyphae or an special reproductive hyphae called sporangiophores. The zoospores are reniform and biflagellate and the flagellae are inserted laterally. One flagellum is of whiplash type and the other flagellum is of tinsel type. In advanced forms, the sporangia behave as conidia. Sexual reproduction is oogamous. The oogonium contains a single oosphere which is surrounded by periplasm The antheridium is short and club-shaped. Fertilization is of amphigynous type. The fertilization product is called the oospore which is diploid.

FAMILY—PYTHIACAE

The members are saprophytes or parasites. The live as facultative parasites. The mycelium is aseptate and coenocytic and the hyphae are intracellular. Asexual reproduction in by means of sporangiospores. Sexual reproduction is oogamous.

Genus—Pythium

The genus is world wide in distribution and represented by nearly 90 species. Several species occur as saprophytes in water, in soil or on decaying organic matter in water and parasites of plants. Many species are facultative parasites and cause pre- emergence killing and damping off disease. They mainly parasitize usually seedlings roots, stems and fruits. Pythium debaryanum is a well known species causing damping off of seedlings in tobacco, tomato, mustards and chillies. The fungus lives saprophytically in the moist humus soil and attacks the seedling at the soil level. Thereafter it lives as a parasite.

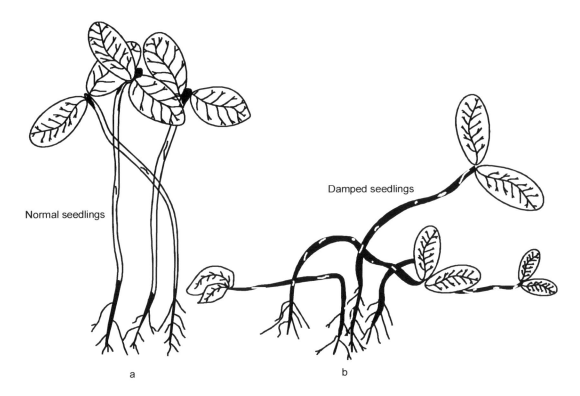

Figure 6.1 (a–b) Pythium sp. a—Normal Seedlings; b—Infected Seedlings

Symptoms The damping off disease affects the young seedlings in patches in the seed bed. After the infection there is rapid killing of cells and collapse of the tissue of the hypocoty1. The infected tissue appears soft and water soaked. The young seedlings are completely killed and the plumule and radicle undergo complete rotting. The infected seedlings soon tumble down on the ground. From the point of attack, the disease spreads in ever widening circles (Figure 6.1 a–b).

Vegetative structure Mycelium is richly branched, hyphae are slender cylindrical, hyaline and coenocytic. The septa may develop at the time of reproduction and in old hyphae. The mycelium lives saprophytically or parasitically. It lives saprophytically on dead organic matter in the soil. Parasitically it grows in the young seedling. The hyphae many be both intracellular as well as intercellular when intracellular haustoria are lacking.

Reproduction Reproduction occurs before the death of the seedling. Reproduction is both asexual and sexual.

Asexual reproduction It takes place by means of zoospores which are produced in small, globular, or oval, sac-like sporangia. They are formed singly and terminally at the ends of somatic hyphae. There are no specialized sporangiophores. Three types of sporangia ar recognised

1. **Filamentous sporangia**   In simpler forms, the sporangia are not much differentiated from the vegetative hyphae. They are slender, simple or branched filaments of the same size as the vegetative hyphae, e.g., *P. gracile.*

2. **Lobulated sporangia**   The sporangia are like inflated lobed hyphae, e.g., *P. aphanidermatam.*

3. **Globose sporangia**   The sporangia are globose in *P. debaryanum.* A terminal or intercalary portion of a hypha enlarges and becomes spherical in shape. It then cuts off by a cross wall. The sporangium is a multinucleated structure and is filled with hyaline cytoplasm containing numerous nuclei. Sporangium germinates by two ways

a. *Indirect germination of sporangium*   Under wet conditions, the sporangium functions as zoosporangium. The mature zoosporangium puts out a narrow, papilla-like out growth called the exit tube. The apex of the exit tube swells into a thin walked vesicle and the protoplasm migrates into the vesicle. Cleavage of cylopasm occurs to form many uninucleated zoospores. Finally the wall of the vesicle breaks downs and the zoospores swim away. The zoospores are biflagellate and reniform and the two flagella are laterally attached. After swimming for sometime, the zoospore encysts and germinates by germ tube to form a new mycelium.

b. *Direct gemination of sporangium*   The sporangia are detached form the hyphae and are blown by wind or by water. On falling on a suitable host, the sporangium germinattes like a conidium. If the temperature is above the optimum, it directly puts out a germ tube which enters into the host either through the stoma or through the epidermal cell. The germ tube grows and branches to form a mycelium.

Sexual reproduction   It is oogumous and takes place at the end of the growing season. The sex organs are formed within the dead tissues of the host. The male sex organ is the antheridium and the female sex organ is called the oogonium. They are developed in close proximity on separate short lateral hyphae arising from the same mycelium. Many species are homothaltic. Some species are heterothallic e.g., *P. heterothallicum.*

The young oogonium has a thin wall and is a multinucleated structure. In the mature oogonium the protoplastt is differenciated into two zones such as outer periplasm and inner ooplasm. Periplasm is the narrow outer zone lining the oogonial wall. It has several nuclei. The ooplasm is the large central portion of the oogonium and it is filled with dense cytoplasm. It has a single nucleus and is filled with reserve food materials. The unicucleate oophasm functions as as oosphere or egg.

The antheridium develops terminally on a short antheridial branch arising laterally either from the oogonial stalk or a neighbouring hypha. The antheridium comes in contact with the oogonial wall and flattens against it. Antheridium is an elongated, club, shaped structure and is smaller than the oogonium. Young antheridia are multinucleate but all, except one nucleus degenerate at maturity. It forms a single male gamete.

Fertilization   Fertilization is paragynous. During fertilization, the falttened tip of the antheridium puts out a fine fertilization tube which penterates the oogonial wall through the pore, pierces the periplasm and dips into the ooplasm. One nucleus is transferred into the ooplasm. Karyogamy between male nucleus and egg occurs and remaining nuclei of antheridia and oogonial periplasm degenerate. The fertilized egg secretes a thick wall and has plenty of reserve food materials. It is transformed into a diploid oospore. The oospores may undergo a period of rest for several weeks before they geminate.

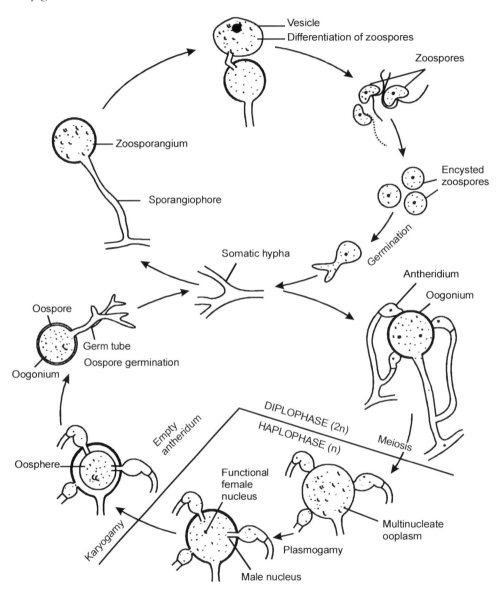

Figure 6.2 Life cycle of *Pythium debaryanum* (Modified from Alexopoulos and Mims)

Germination of oospore During favourable conditions of growth, the oospore germinates. It imbibes water and swells and the germ tube emerges out. Meiosis occurs in the diploid nucleus.

It may either grow into a small hypha and infects the host or the tip of the hypha swells to form a vesicle-like sporangium. The contents of the oospore migrates into the vesicle. It either behaves like the zoosporangium producing zoospores or it behaves like a conidium and germinates directly by putting out a germ tube (Figure 6.2).

Control of the disease The seeds are treated with a seed protectant such as Blitox-50 and Arasan. The chemical forms a protective layer external to the seed coat. Thin sowing in done to avoid over crowding. The seed beds should be exposed to air and light. Excessive moisture in the seed bed should be avoided. Atmospheric humidity should be lowered. The soil of the nursery should be treated with dilute formaldehyde solution and Bordeaux mixture.

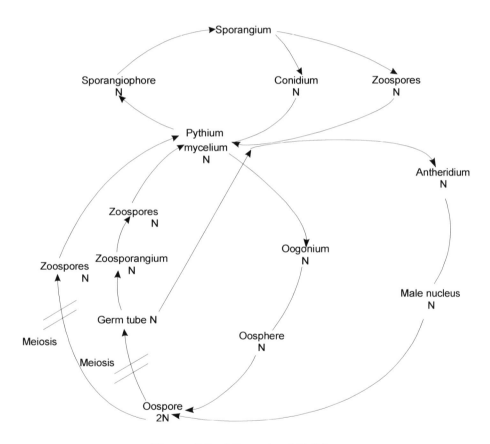

Figure 6.3 Life cycle of *Pythium*

There is no alternation of generation in the life cycle. The life cycle is haplontic since there is a prolonged haploid phase and the diplophase is very much reduced. It is represented only by the diploid oospore. Meiosis occurs during the germination of oospore and thus it is called zygotic meiosis (Figure 6.3).

Genus—*Albugo* (*Cystopus*)

The genus has nearly 30 species. From India nearly 18 species have been reported of which the most common species is *Albugo candida* (*Cystopus candidus*) causing white rust or blister rust of crucifers like radish, turnip, cabbage, mustards, etc. *A. bliti* infects members of Amaranteceae. The disease appears in the form of shiny, white, smooth raised, irregular blisters on the leaves or stem (Figure 6.4).

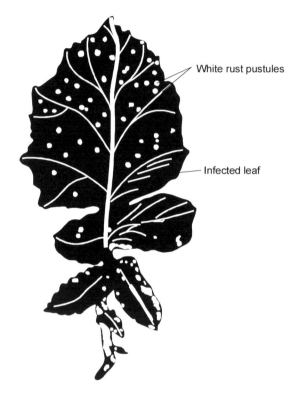

White rust pustules

Infected leaf

Figure 6.4   Infected radish leaf showing pustules of white rust (*Albugo candida*)

The root is not attacked. The patches gradually turn powdery. It also causes deformation of flowers and fruits of the host. The distortion and hypertrophy of infected inflorescence is the most conspicuous symptom of the disease. There is hypertrophy of individual cells of affected tissues (Figure 6.5).

Figure 6.5 Diseased plant of *Capsella* bearing white pustules of *Albugo candida*. The stem is distorted as a result of infection

Systematic position

Division: Mycota

Subdivision: Mastigomycotina

Class : Oomycetes

Order : Peronosporales

Family : Albuginaceae

Mycelium   The thallus is eucarpic and mycelium consists of branched aseptate, coenocytic and intercellular hyphae sending small knob-like haustoria into the host cells. The hyphal wall contains cellulose and not chitin. The fine structure of haustorium is studied by Berlin and Bowen (1964). The lomasomes are more numerous within the plasma membrane than in the hyphae. The haustorium consists of two parts namely the haustorial stalk or neck and haustorial head or body. In the haustorisl head, the cytoplasm is densely packed with mitochondria, ribosomes, ER and lipid inclusions but nuclei have not been observed. The haustorial stalk is surrounded by a collar like sheath which is an extension of the host cell wall.

Asexual reproduction   When the mycelium matures it produces pads of hyphal at certain areas just below the epidermis. The lips of the hyphae constituting the mat grow vertically into short upright thick walled unbranched club-shaped structures called the sporangiophores. They develop as a palisade like layer between the epidermies and mesophyll of the host leaf. Each sporangiophore is cylindrical and produces a chain of spherical sporangia in basipetal succession (Figure 6.6). It shows blastic mode of sporangial development. The sporangial initial arises as a bud at its apex. It contains about 4–6 nuclei and dense cytoplasm. The sporangial insitial is delimited by a basal septum near the sporogenous locus. It becomes the first sporangium and the oldest in the chain. Then a new sporangial initially grows on a bud from the sporogenous locus and when it grows into the normal size it is also delimited by the formation of the basal septum. This process is repeated to form a chain of sporangia. The middle layer of the septum between the sporangium is dissolved to form the connective or disjunctor between the successive sporangia in the chain (Figure 6.7 a–f).

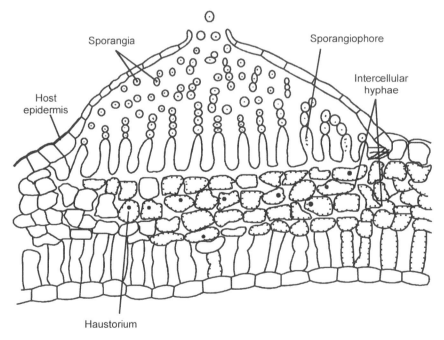

Figure 6.6   *Albugo candida.* A section of host leaf passing through the sporangial sorus

The sporangia are small hyaline spherical structures with a smooth or punctate surface. The basipetal arrangement of sporangia in the chain helps in the ready dispersal of the oldest sporangia by air or rain water and proper nourishment of the younger ones. Due to pressure of the developing chain of sporangia, host epidermis is raised and finally ruptured. If the sporangium matures connection or gelatinous pads between them dry, shrink and finally disintegrate in moist air. Thus the sporangia in the chain are separated (Figure 6.6).

Sporangium shows indirect and direct germination depending on temperature conditions. In the presence of moisture and low temperature the sporangium functions as a zoosporangium. Each sporangium produces about four to eight biflagellate zoospores. After swimming for sometime zoospore encysts and forms a germ tube which penetrates the host epidermis. In the presence of high temperature and dry conditions, the sporangium behaves like a conidium. It germinates directly to form a germ tube which penetrates the host through a stroma or the epidermis.

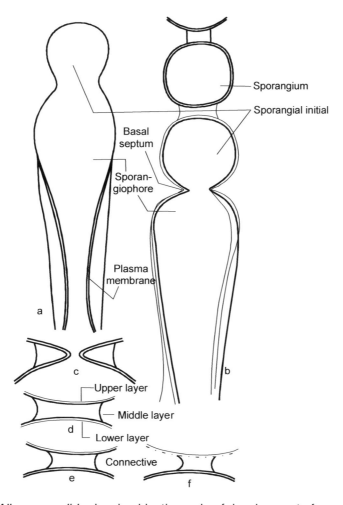

Figure 6.7 (a–f) *Albugo candida* showing blastic mode of development of sporangia (After Khan)

Sexual reproduction   It is typically oogemous. Sex organs develop in the intercellular spaces deeper in the host tissues. Both oogonia and antheridia develop terminally from separate female and male hyphae. They are multinucleated form the beginning. The oogonia are globular. The antheridia are clavate and develop in close proximity to oogonia and is attached usually laterally (i.e.,) paragynous. When young, each oogonium contains six to twelve nuclei. The nuclei divide mitotically and increase in number as the oogonium matures. The contents of oogonium become differentiated into periplasm and ooplasm. Only one functional nucleus remains in the ooplasm and this forms the egg or female nucleus and the rest of the nuclei move into he periplasm. Though the anthridium

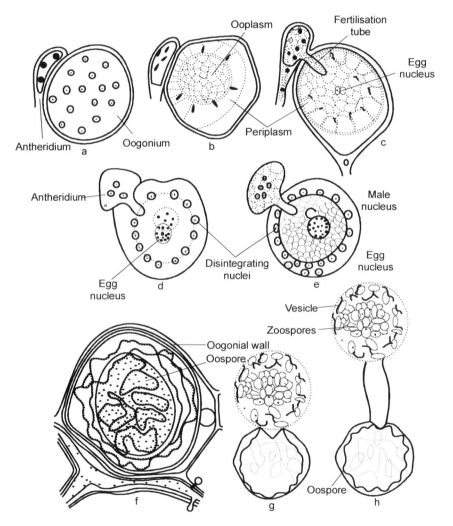

Figure 6.8   (a–h) Stages in sexual reproduction of *Albugo candida*. (a–e)—Ddevelopment of sex organ f—Oogonium containing a thick walled oospore, (g,h)—Two methods of oospore germination.

contains many nuclei only one nucleus is functional at maturity. Plasmogamy takes place by gametangial contact, where the male nucleus from antheridium is transferred to oogonium through the fertilization tube. Karyogamy occurs and a thin membrane develops around the diploid zygote, the oospore. The wall of the oospore becomes thickened and it is warty or tuberculate or it may have network of ridges or other patterns. Oospore undergoes a prolonged resting period.

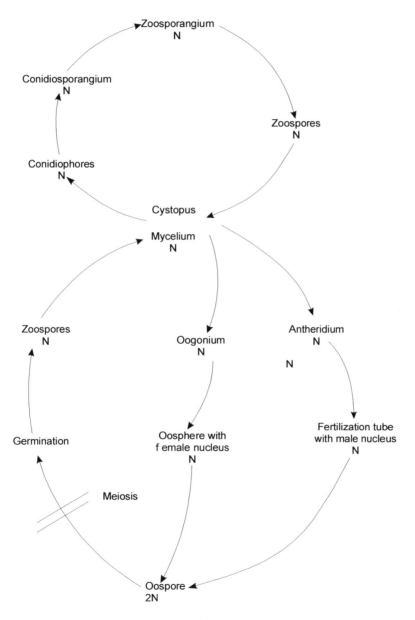

Figure 6.9 Life cycle *Albugo*

During favourable conditions the oospore germinates. The diploid nucleus undergoes meiosis to form four nuclei. These divide repeatedly to many many nuclei. Numerous uninucleate daughter protoplasts result and each is metamorphosed into a biflagellate zoospore. The oospore wall cracks and a germ tube emerges which ends in a thin vesicle. From the oospore, the zoospores pass into the vesicle. Soon the vesicle bursts liberating the zoospores. Sometimes the oospore shows direct germination by putting forth one or more germ tubes which penetrate the host. (Figure 6.8 a–h).

Control of white rust disease   Rotation of crops, removal and destruction of infected plants from the field and spraying with fungicides such as with 0.8% Bordeaux mixture are the most effective methods of controlling the disease.

The life cycle is haplontic with a prolonged haploid phase and and the diplophase is represented by the diploid oospore. There is zygotic meiosis which occurs during the germination of zoospores. There is no alternation of generation (Figure 6.9).

7

SUBDIVISION—ZYGOMYCOTINA

GENERAL CHARACTERISTICS

The fungi included in this group are terrestrial. Thallus is usually mycelial and the hyphae are branched and aseptate. It is coenocytic. Hyphal cell wall mainly consists of chitin and chitosan. The thallus is haploid. Asexual reproduction takes place by the formation of non-motile spores called aplanospore. Sexual reproduction is by gametangial copulation, typically isogumous and the product of sexual reproduction is called the zygospore and it is the post-fertilization product. It is also called a perfect state spore. This subdivision has two classes such as **Zygomycetes** and **Trichomycetes**.

Class–Zygomycetes

These are terrestrial moulds which show a wide range in habit. Most of them are saprophytes. Some are soil saprophytes and others are coprophilous. The mycelium is aseptate and well-developed. Non-motile sporangiospores are formed during asexual reproduction. Sexual reproduction is by gametangial copulation which produces a zygospore.

Order–Mucorales

Most of them are soil saprophytes and a few are weak parasites of fruits and animals. Mycelium is coenocytic, aseptate and haploid.

Genus–*Mucor*

There are nearly 60–80 species of *Mucor* and are called terrestrial moulds. Most of them are saprophytes on a variety of materials including foodstuff. Under moist conditions, they cause spoilage of bread, jams, jellies, syrups, sugary food stuff, leather, etc. Some are weak parasites of fruits and vegetables. Some species such as *M. mucedo* and *M. racemosus* are the common contaminants of air.

Systematic Position

Division:	Mycota
Subdivision:	Zygomycotina
Class:	Zygomyectes
Order:	Mucorales
Family:	Mucoraceae

Thallus The thallus is eucarpic and mycelial. The hyphae are cottony white, grey or brownish, coenocytic and richly branched; the branches usually tapering to fine points. In anaerobic liquid culture especially in the presence of carbondioxide, *Mucor* may grow as yeast-like form which reverts to filamentous form in presence of oxygen. The mycelium is differentiated into,

i. absorptive hyphae which penetrate the substratum

ii. aerial hyphae.

The absorptive hyphae are called the rhizoidal hyphae and they are helpful in anchoring the mycelium and absorption of food materials. The aerial hyphae are involved in reproduction and the sporangiophores arise from this (Figure 7.1 a–c).

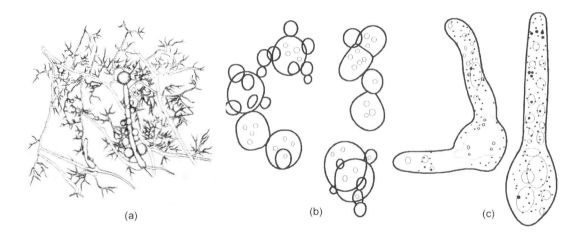

(a) (b) (c)

Figure 7.1 a–c. Somatic stages of *Mucor*. a—Mycelium and young sporangiophore of *M. mucedo*. Note the lipid globules attached with sporangiophore, b—Yeastlike growth of *M. rouxii* in liquid medium under anaerobic conditions, c—Filamentous growth of *M. rouxii* from spores in liquid medium under aerobic conditions

Asexual reproduction It takes place by the following methods.

1. **Fragmentation** Vegetative hyphae break up into smaller fragments and each fragment develops into new mycelium.

2. **Chlamydospores** These are thick-walled mycelial segments arising from the mycelium. These segments become rounded and secrete a thick wall. It can survive during unfavourable conditions. Under suitable conditions, they germinate to form new mycelium.

Sporangiospores This is the most common method of asexual reproduction. The sporangia develop terminally on hyphal branches called sporangiophores. They are simple and unbranched. The apex of the sporangiophore swells and cytoplasmic mass along with nuclei move into this. This is the young sporangium. On maturity the contents of sporangium become differentiated into thick dense layer of cytoplasm with many nuclei towards the peripheral region beneath the sporangial wall and a vacuolated portion towards the centre. A dome-shaped septum is laid down cutting off a distal peripheral portion from a central cylindrical or sub-globose core, the columella. The contents of the distal portion is called the sporiferous zone. It undergoes cleavage to form a number of multinucleate segments and these segments round off to form sporangiospores (Figure 7.2 a–b).

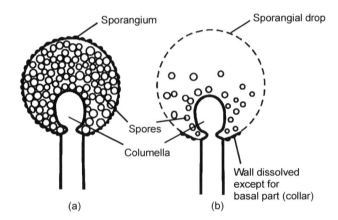

Figure 7.2 (a–b) Asexual reproduction in *Mucor mucedo*. a—Immature sporangium with columella and sporangial wall, b—Dehisced sporangium to show collar (frill) and sporangiospores

When the sporangia are mature the sporangiophores may be seen as a blunt-tipped aerial hyphae growing away from the substratum. The sporangial wall dissolves except for basal region where its remnants can be seen as a frill or collar at the base of the columella. The sporangiospores are dark, usually elliptic to ovoid and are non-motile. The spores are minute and light and are dispersed by air under dry or unsuitable conditions. The spores remain viable for a long period. When they fall on a suitable substratum in presence of proper moisture and temperature they germinate by germ tubes to form new mycelium.

Sexual reproduction Sexual reproduction is by gametangial copulation and is isogamous. The fusing gametangia are identical and coenocytic. Some species are homothallic but, most are heterothallic. In heterothallic species zygospores are formed only when mycelium of compatible strains come in contact with each other. The phenomenon of heterothallism, i.e., occurrence of different compatible strains of mycelia was discovered in Mucorales by A.E. Blakeslee in 1904 (Figure 7.3 a–f).

In the heterothallic species of *Mucor* such as *M. mucedo* and *M. hiemalis*, the sexual act is initiated when hyphal branches of (+) and (–) strains come in contact with each other. Each branch swells at its tip to develop a progametangium. Dense cytoplasm and numerous nuclei flow to the contacting tips which enlarge further. A septum thus separates the terminal part of the gametangium from the remaining part of he progametangium, the suspensor. Since gametangia are undifferentiated mass of multinucleate protoplast, they are called coenogametangia. As the gametangia mature, the separating wall dissolves and the protoplast of both mix with each other. Nuclear fusion occurs between nuclei of (+) and (–) strains to give numerous diploid nuclei in each zygospore. The young zygospore, containing many diploid nuclei lies within the parent gametangial wall. It later enlarges and secretes several layered thick wall around it. As the zygospore matures, it breaks up the original gametangial wall into fragments which fall apart exposing the zygospore. The wall of mature zygospore is probably five-layered, two layers in the outer exospores and three in the inner endospore. The zygospore germinates after a long period of rest. During germination, the outer wall cracks and the inner wall comes out in the form of a germsporangiophore which bears a single terminal germsporangium. The contents of the germsporangium is cleaved to form many spores (Figure 7.4).

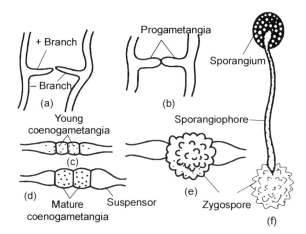

Figure 7.3   (a–f) Stages in sexual reproduction of *Mucor*. (a–d)—Development of coenogametangia, e—A mature zygospore, f—Germinating zygospore

Physiology of sexual reproduction in Mucorales   Details of this have already been described in the chapter hormonal involvement in sexual reproduction in fungi. When two compatible strains approach each other, three reactions can be distinguished (Burgeff, 1920, Mesland *et al.*, 1974).

1. *Zygophore induction*   It is a telomorphic reaction which involves the induction of aerial zygophore. Zygophores in both (+) and (–) strains are induced by the hormones Trisporic acid B and C. These acids are oxidized, unsaturated derivates of Trimethyl cyclohexane. They are produced in large numbers only when (+) and (–) cultures are in continuous diffusion contact with each other. The strains first produce small quantities of prohormones that are converted to Trisporic acids.

2. *Zygotropic reaction*   It involves directed growth of zygophores of (+) and (–) mating partners towards each other. It is a chemotropic response. Mesland *et al.* (1974) have shown that the vegetative

mycelium of *M. mucedo* even when not in diffusion contact with vegetative mycelium of opposite strain could produce volatile substances which induced zygophore development and the zygotrophic reaction. These volatile substances have a dual role to enhance Trisporic acid synthesis in the opposite mating type and to mediate the zygotropic response.

3. *Thigmotropic reaction*   It involves the events which occur after contact of the respective zygophores such as gametangial fusion and septation.

Life cycle is haplontic with many haplophases and the only diplophase is the zygospore. Meiosis occurs in the zygospore during germination. There is no alternation of generation (Figure 7.5).

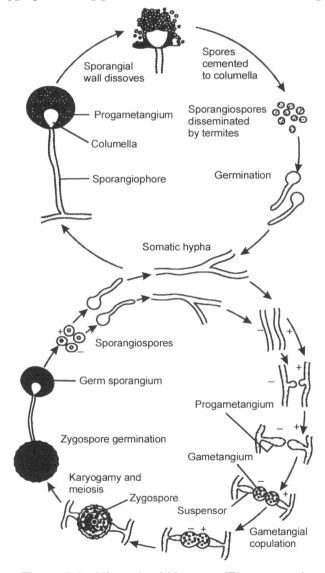

Figure 7.4   Life cycle of *Mucor* sp. (Plasmogamy)

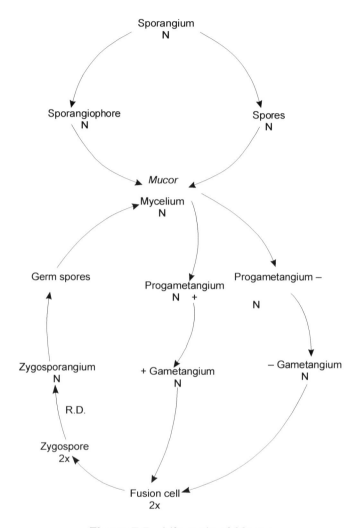

Figure 7.5 Life cycle of *Mucor*

Genus—*Pilobolus*

Pilobolus sps. is commonly called hat-thrower referring to the mechanism of sporangial discharge. Most of the species of *Pilobolus* are coprophilous found growing on dung or excretory matter of herbivores like horse, cow, sheep, rabbit and deer . A few species also occur in soil. About 10 species are reported in India. *P. longipes* and *P.crystatinus* are most common.

Coprophilous fungi can be easily cultured by using dung as a substratum. If fresh dung is incubated in a moist Petri dish near the window of laboratory, within 3–4 days appear characteristic bulbous sporangiophores.

Systematic position

Division: Mycota

Subdivision: Zygomycotina

Class: Zygomycetes

Order: Mucorales

Family: Pilobolaceae

Thallus The thallus is eucarpic and mycelial, hyphae are coenocytic, aseptate, branched and are mostly submerged in the substratum (Figure 7.6 a and b) .

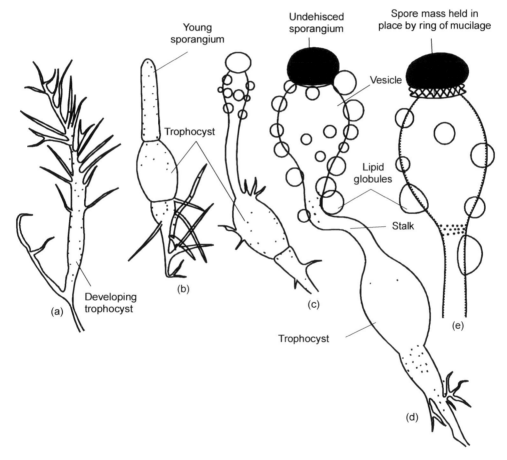

Figure 7.6 (a–e)—Asexual reproduction in *Pilobolus*. a—Developing trophocyst, having carotene-rich cytoplasm. b—Immature sporangiophore developing from trophocyst, c—Further development of sporangium. d—Trophocyst bearing undehisced sporangium, e—Sporangiophore bearing a sporangium which has dehisced at its base (where the spore mass is held in a mucilage ring)

Asexual reproduction   It takes place by the formation of aplanospores which are produced within the sporangia. Some hypae grow out of the substratum and become upright. These are called sporangiophores. Each sporangiophore develops from a characteristic swelling called the trophocyst. This trophocyst is generally embedded in the substratum. The sporangiophore of *Pilobolus* is made up of three parts; a basal swollen carotene-rich trophocyst, an elongated stipe and a sub-sporangial vesicle. The trophocyst is ovate, cylindrical, napiform or globose in shape. The sporangiophore grown away from the trophocyst during day time (or) towards the light and its tip enlarges during night to form the sporangium. The subsporangial vesicle is pyriform much larger than the sporangium and consist of a single large vacuole which completely fills it except for a thin layer of protoplasm adjacent to the wall. The subsporangia vesicle bears a somewhat flattened, black and heavily cutinized sporangia. A conical columella lies at the bottom of a sporangium, which is separated from the spores by a pad of mucilage. The contents of sporangium by cleavage give rise to many non motile spores. Each sporangium consist of about 15,000 to 30,000 spores.

The sporangiophore is highly phototrophic and the stripe will bend in the direction of light until the sporangium faces the light directly. Consequently the sporangia shoot towards light.

Discharge of the sporangia is an interesting phenomeon in *Pilobolus*. The swelling of subsporangial vesicle plays an important role in sporangial discharge. The vesicle is turgid containing a liquid under pressure. Drops of excited liquid commonly adheres to the sporangiophore. The sub-sporangial vesicle explodes transversely at a line of weakness just break the columella. It is accompanied by a sudden contraction of the walls of the sporangiophore, sub-sporangial vesicle and trophocyst which results in the squiring out of the cell sap from the open mouth of the sub-sporangial vesicle (Figure 7.6 c–e).

The cell sap at first squirts out from the sub-sporangial vesicle as the continuous jet, but later it breaks up into several separate drops. The drop at the top in the largest travels farthest and adheres to the under, wettable and gelatinous side of the sporangium. This carries the sporangium at a speed of 10–20 feet per second through the air. When the sporangium strikes an object, it becomes attached to it with the help of a mucilaginous ring and is surrounded by the cell sap. The cell sap later dries up and the sporangium becomes more firmly attached with its dorsal side facing outward. In this condition it is difficult for the sporangium to get detached from the vegetation. When eaten by herbivores, the spores are released in the animal gut by the sporangium and are disseminated by dung (Figure 7.7 a–d).

The production of sporangia is a rhythmic phenomenon requiring alternate light and dark periods. Successful crops of sporangia appear each morning at a definite interval of 24 hours. This is an example of circadian rhythm or 24 hours biological clock.

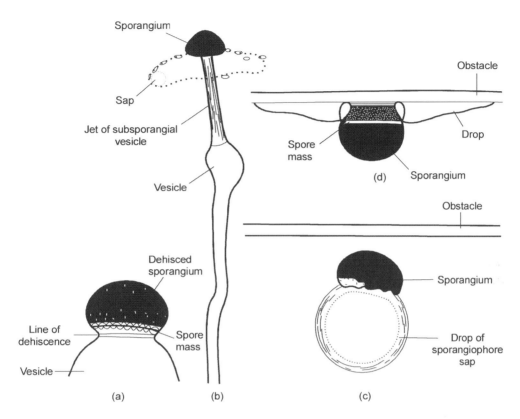

Figure 7.7 a–d. Dehiscence and mechanism of sporangial dispersal in *Pilobolus*. a—Sporangium showing dehiscence line at its base, b—Sporangiophore projecting a sporangium. Note the jet of liquid. c—Sporangium with adherent drop of sporangiophore sap about to strike an obstacle, d—Sporangium after striking the obstacle. The sporangiophore sap has flown around the sporangium which has turned outwards so that mucilage ring adheres to the surface of the obstacle

Sexual reproduction Sexual reproduction is rare in *Pilobolus*, occurring under some abnormal conditions only. Most species are heterothallic. Two neighbouring hyphae become club-shaped and rich in protoplasm. They are called progametangia which grow upright and lie side by side to each other. Apical cell in each progametangium is cut off by a transverse wall. These two terminal cells are called the gametangia and are rich in cytoplasm. The rest of the progametangium is called the suspensor. Sexual reproduction is by gametangial copulation and isogametes. Walls between the gametangia dissolve and their protoplasm mix with each other. Nuclear unites in pairs in the common cell, formed by the conjugation of gametangia. Then diploid fusion cell enlarges into a zygospore. The zygospore wall is thick, smooth and light brown to black. During germination, it germinates either by putting forth a germ tube or by producing a germ sporangium containing spores (Figure 7.8 a–d).

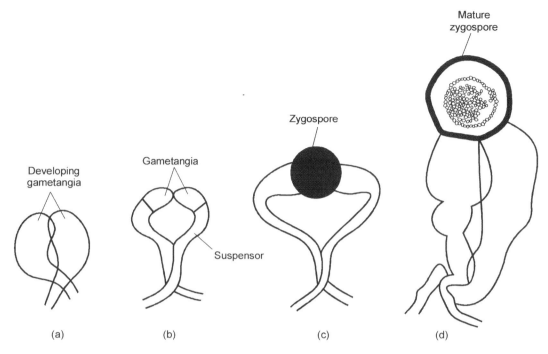

Figure 7.8   a–d. Stages in sexual reproduction of *Pilobolus*

8

SUBDIVISION—ASCOMYCOTINA

GENERAL CHARACTERISTICS

The Ascomycotina is the largest group of fungi and contains 2,720 genera and 28,650 species which include a wide range of diverse organisms. Most of them are terrestrial and the majority are saprobes, some are parasites of insects and other animals and some are pathogenic causing serious plant diseases.

Somatic Structures

Except for some yeasts, these fungi possess well-developed septate and profusely branched mycelium with one or several nuclei. In yeast, the thallus is unicellular. The cell wall largely contains chitin and cellulose is generally absent. The septum is perforated by a simple pore through which cytoplasmic continuity between adjacent cell segments occur. The pore is wide enough to allow nuclei and mitochondria to pass through.

Aggregation of modified vegetative hyphae may lead to the production of structures known as sclerotia. In some forms rhizomorphs are formed by aggregation of mycelial strands. Stomata are also produced in some members.

Asexual reproduction　It occurs by the formation of non-motile structures called conidia. Conidia are exogenously produced, non-motile, deciduous asexual spores. These are borne on a simple or branched hypha, the conidiophore. The conidiophore is unicellular or multicellular. Normally the conidia are produced in basipetal chains. Other methods such as fragmentation, budding, fission, conidia production are also common. Asexual stage of Ascomycotina is referred to as the imperfect stage in the life cycle.

Sexual reproduction　Members of Ascomycotina are homothallic as well as heterothallic. In heterothallic species, the compatibility is of bipolar type, i.e., governed by a single gene with two alleles such as 'A' and 'a'. Plasmogamy occurs by,

i.   gametangial copulation (in Hemiascomycetes as yeast)

ii. gametangial contact (in Plectomycetes as *Erysiphe*, *Apergillus* and *Penicillium*) (Figure 8.1).

iii. spermatization (in Pyrenomycetes as *Neurospora* and *Mycosphaerella*)

iv. somatogamy (in Discomyates as *Peziza* and *Morchella*).

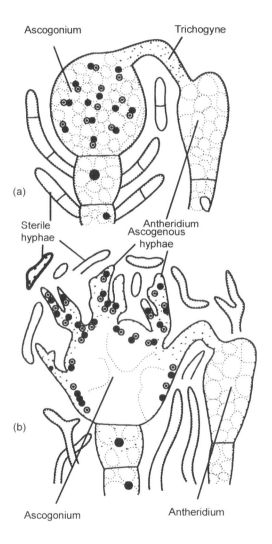

Figure 8.1   Ascomycetes. Plasmogamy by gametangial contact and post-plasmogamy changes. (a) V.S. of sex organs after migration of male nuclei into the ascogonium. (b) A later stage showing the arrangement of male and female nuclei in pairs (dikaryons) in the peripheral cytoplasm of the ascogonium, origin of ascogenous hyphae and the passage of paired nuclei into the ascogenous hyphae. (Diagrammatic)

One of the interesting features of the sexual reproduction of Ascomycotina is the separation of plasmogamy and karyogamy in space and time except in Hemiascomycetes. These two nuclei which lie together during plasmogamy do not fuse immediately but remain paired and form a dikaryon. The dikaryon gives rise to more dikaryons by successive conjugate or simultaneous divisions until karyogamy takes place.

Development of ascus   Asci develop in two ways.

1. *Direct development of ascus*   In lower Ascomycotina like yeasts, the compatible nuclei are brought together in a fusion cell by plasmogamy. The two nuclei fuse (karyogamy) immediately to form a diploid cell, the zygote. This zygote enlarges directly to form the ascus.

The diploid cell behaves as an ascus mother cell. Diploid nucleus undergoes meiosis which is followed by mitosis to form eight haploid nuclei. Cytoplasm gathers around each nucleus, and each protoplast secretes a wall around it to form an ascospore. Some asci are four-spored. The ascospores are formed by free cell formation and not by cleavage. The asci are not enclosed by any protective sheath of sterile hyphae. Thus there is no formation of any fruit body or ascocarp. Asci are naked and are scattered among the vegetative hyphae.

2. *Indirect development of ascus*   In higher Ascomycotina, there is a long interval between plasmogamy and karyogamy. After the transfer of male nuclei to ascogonium, the male and female nuclei arrange themselves in pair and these pairs of nuclei are called dikaryons. From the ascogonium, special hyphae known as ascogenous hyphae are formed. Ascogenous hyphae are branched or unbranched and the terminal cell of the ascogenous hyphae give rise to asci by crozier formation (Figure 8.2 a–b).

Crozier formation   The tip of ascogenous hyphae becomes curved to form a crozier. The dikaryon undergoes one conjugate division to form two dikaryons. Two septa are formed in such a way to form three cells such as (i) a penultimate binucleate cell, the ascus mother cell (ii) an anti-penultimate cell which is haploid stalk, (iii) a stalk ultimate cell which is haploid. In the dikaryotic ascus mother cell, the two nuclei fuse and the diploid nucleus immediately undergoes meiosis to form four haploid nuclei. These nuclei again divide mitotically to form eight haploid nuclei. During this time the ascus elongates. Cytoplasm aggregates around each nucleus to form a haploid ascospore. Some cytoplasm is unused and is known as epiplasm. Thus the diploid phase is very much reduced and is transitory (Figure 8.2 a–i).

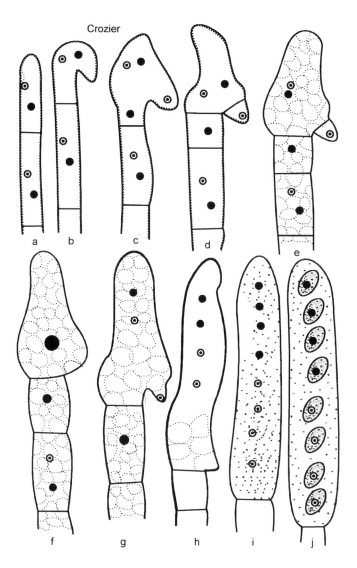

Figure 8.2 (a–j). Ascomycetes. Stages in the development of ascus (a–f) and differentiation of ascopores (g–j). (a) Tip of ascogenous hypha; (b), End cell curled over to form a hook or crozier; (c) The two nuclei in the hook or crozier undergo conjugate division to form four daughter nuclei; (d) Uninucleate terminal hook cell, binucleate arch cell (or penultimate cell) and uninucleate stalk of ultipenultimate cell cut off; (e) Binucleate arch cell elongates to form an ascus mother cell and the uninucleate terminal or ultimate cell beginning to abort; (f) Two nuclei in the ascus mother cell fuse to form a synkaryon; (g)–(h) Denote meiosis; (i) After the third (mitotic) division; (j) Mature ascus with eight ascospores arranged in a uniseriate manner.

Asci and ascospores   In all members of Ascomycotina, ascospores are produced in a saclike ascus. Ascus may be globose, club-shaped or cylindrical. The ascospores may be arranged in uniseriate, biseriate or fasciculate manner. The ascospores are released by breakdown of the ascus wall. In most forms, the asci are enclosed by a definite wall called the peridium and this forms the ascocarp. The wall of the ascus is single (unitunicate) or double (bitunicate). Unitunicate asci may be inoperculate or operculate. In inoperculate asci there is no operculum or cap at the tip. Ascospores are liberated through a slit. In operculate asci, the ascus tip is surrounded by an operculum or cap. The operculum is blown aside by the force of explosion.

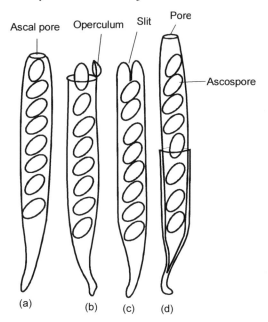

Figure 8.3   (a–d). Ascomycetes. Various types of ascal dehiscence

Dehiscence of ascus   Dehiscence of ascus is variable. In Ascomycotina, the ascospores are ejected forcibly usually with a puffing action. The glycogen present in the epiplasm becomes rapidly transformed into sugars of high osmotic value. Such a transformation results in absorption of water. Thus a pressure is setup in the ascus which tears the ascal wall with the sudden explosion. The ascospores are ejected forcibly into the air and are dispersed by wind.

The ascospores are variable in size, shape and colour. They are generally elliptical and in some they are spherical. In some they are long, narrow and the wall of the ascospore is thin and two-layered such as the outer epispore and inner endospore (Figure 8.3 a–d).

Fruit bodies (Ascocarps)   Ascocarps are the post-fertilization products of Ascomycotina. Only in hemiascomycetes (yeasts), ascocarps are not produced and asci are naked. As a result of sexual reproduction, the neighbouring vegetative hyphae and those growing from the sex organs grow rapidly and become interwoven into a plectenchymatous mass. This mass of hyphae surround the developing asci. The whole structure, i.e., the asci and the protective vegetative hyphae develop into an ascocarp. The types of ascocarps are dealt in the general account (Figure 8.4).

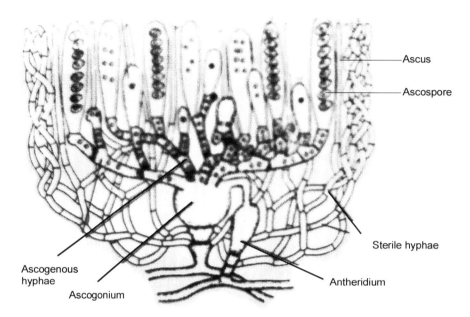

Ascus

Ascospore

Sterile hyphae

Antheridium

Ascogenous hyphae

Ascogonium

Figure 8.4 Ascomycetes. Section through a young ascocarp showing the sexual apparatus, and arrangement of ascogenous and sterile hyphae—Diagrammatic

Classification of Ascomycotina

1. **Hemiascomycetes**   No ascocarps and ascogenous hyphae; asci naked; thallus yeastlike or mycelial.

2. **Loculoascomycetes**   Ascocarp and ascogenous hyphae present; thallus mycelial, asci bitunicate; fruit body an ascostroma.

3. **Plectomycetes**   Ascocarp and ascogenous hyphae present; thallus mycelial; asci unitunicate, evanescent, i.e., break down at maturity and fruit body, a cleistothecium.

4. **Laboulbeniomycetes**   Ascocarp and ascogenous hyphae present; thallus reduced; asci unitunicate, inoperculate; ascocarp a perithecium; exoparasites of arthropods.

5. **Pyrenomycetes**   Ascocarp and ascogenous hyphae present; thallus reduced; asci unitunicate; fruit body a perithecium and asci are inoperculate.

6. **Discomycetes**   Ascocarp and ascogenous hyphae present; thallus mycelial; asci unitunicate, ascocarp an apothecium; asci operculate.

9

CLASS—HEMIASCOMYCETES

GENERAL CHARACTERISTICS

The thallus is yeastlike or mycelial. Asexual reproduction is by budding or fission. Sexual reproduction is by gametangial copulation in which plasmogamy is soon followed by karyogamy. Asci are naked and ascogenous hyphae and ascocarps are lacking. Yeasts are mostly saprophytic and Taphrinales are parasitic.

ORDER—ENDOMYCETALES

Some of Endomycetales are saprophytic and others are parasitic. The thallus is greatly reduced to a single cell. Asexual reproduction is by budding or fission. Sexual reproduction is either by copulation between somatic cells which behave as gametangia or between ascopores. Sometimes zygote develop parthenogenetically. Ascocarps are absent and asci are naked. Yeasts are industrially important and are used in alcohol and bread making.

Genus—*Saccharomyces*

Saccharomyces species are commonly known as yeasts and are employed in bread making and beer brewing. Because of this, these species are called the baker's yeast or brewer's yeast. They occur chiefly on media rich in sugar or an organic matter mostly of vegetable origin. They are ubiquitous saprophytic organisms occurring in air, soil and wherever sugary substrate is available.

Yeasts are the oldest cultivated plants. The microscopic examination of the bread found with Egyptian mummies revealed the presence of yeast cells indicating an old association of these microorganisms with human race. Leeuwenhoek in 1960 described the yeast cells. Louis Pasteur in 1859 established that fermentation was directly associated with the life activities of yeasts. About 40 species of *Saccharomyces* are known, of which the most common is *S. cerevisiae*, the common baker's and brewer's yeast.

Systematic position

Division:	Mycota
Subdivision:	Ascomycotina
Class:	Hemiascomycetes
Order:	Endomycetales
Family:	Endomycetaceae

Yeast culture   A culture of yeast can be prepared in the laboratory by placing a piece of yeast cake or a few grains of dried yeast in a solution of molasses and water or sugar solution. The yeast cells multiply rapidly in any well aerated nutrient solution containing adequate amount of sugar.

Thallus   The thallus is non-mycelial. Thallus is unicellular, sometimes it may form pseudomycelial structures. It consists of a single minute, oval or spherical cell. In others, the cell is elongated, cylindrical or rectangular in shape. In size it ranges from 2 to 8 μ in diameter by 3 to 15 μ in length. The yeast cells appear hyaline in nature. It consists of a tiny mass of protoplast surrounded by a cell wall.

Fine structure of yeast cell is studied. The cell wall is thin, delicate and firm in nature and is distinguished into three layers. The outer layer consists mainly of mannan and some chitin; the middle largely of glucan, and the innermost layer contains protein glucan. Some lipid and phosphate is also present. The skeletal matter of the wall is made up of a random array of microfibril of chitin, glucan and mannan.

The cell membrane or plasma membrane is a unit membrane but it has a series of shallow, elongated pits or invaginations. The protoplast consists of cytoplasm surrounding a minute nucleus. The cytoplasm is differentiated into two portions, an outer thin ectoplasm and an inner dense endoplasm. The endoplasm contains a single, small dense nucleus less than 1μ in diameter. Special staining techniques are used to localize the nucleus. Associated with the nucleus is a single large vacuole. The vacuole is limited by a single membrane, the tonoplast. It contains a solution or suspension of volutin which is a complex material consisting of RNA, lipoprotein and polyphosphates. The nucleus has a nuclear membrane and is distinct from the vacuole. It is situated at one side of the vacuole. The nuclear membrane has pores. Dark staining strands extend from the nucleus around the vacuole. The cytoplasm has organelles like that of typical eukaryotic cells and these are endoplasmic reticulum, ribosome, mitochondria, golgi apparatus and nucleus. The reserve food products in the cytoplasm are in the form of granules of glycogen, oil globules and protein particles. Mitochondria are variable in shape, depending upon the condition of cell growth. They may be spherical, rodlike, threadlike, simple or branched. Under anaerobic conditions, the mitochondria decrease in size and degenerate into tiny spherical or rod-shaped structures lacking cristae. Respiratory deficient mutants, which form smaller colonies than wild forms. Petite mutants, possess fewer mitochondria.

Nutrition   The cells are heterotrophic in their mode of nutrition since they lack chlorophyll. They obtain readymade food material from an external source by living as saprophytes.

The brewer's yeast obtains nutrition in the form of simple sugars in solutions. It gets it from the substratum on which it grows such as bruised ripe fruits, fruit juices, sugar solutions or crushed moistened grains. The nutrient elements required are carbon, hydrogen, oxygen, nitrogen, phosphorus, potassium, sulphur, magnesium, iron, zinc, manganese, copper and molybdenum. The metallic elements function as enzyme activators or components of enzymes in minute traces. Carbon is chiefly obtained from sugar or starch. A vitamin like growth factor is also essential for growth in extremely low concentrations.

The yeast cells secrete enzymes on the substratum. These enzymes are collectively called the zymase. The zymase changes the starch in the substratum into the simple sugars which diffuse into endoplasm through the thin cell membrane. A small percentage of absorbed sugar is used as food and assimilated. When yeast is grown in a well aerated nutrient medium, the rest of the sugar is completely oxidized in normal respiration.

$$C_6H_{12}O_6 + 6O_2 \rightarrow 6CO_2 + 6H_2O + \text{energy}$$

In such a solution, the yeast cells multiply rapidly. In the absence or poor supply (scarcity) of oxygen the yeast plants multiply slowly. The major portion of sugar is converted into carbondioxide and ethyl alcohol within the cytoplasm. The reaction is shown below

$$C_6H_{12}O_6 + \text{yeast} \rightarrow 2C_2H_5OH + 2CO_2 + \text{energy}$$
$$\text{(Glucose)} \qquad \text{(Ethyl alcohol)}$$

The products of this reaction (CO_2 and C_2H_5OH) diffuse out, through the cell wall into the surrounding liquid. The breakdown of carbohydrates (starch and sugars) by yeast into carbondioxide and alcohol in the absence of oxygen is called alcoholic fermentation. This process is utilized in the production of industrial alcohol, in wine making, in brewing and in bread making. The energy released is utilized by the cell to carry out the vital functions.

Growth   It occurs by an overall increase in size.

Reproduction   Yeast reproduces both asexually and sexually.

Asexual reproduction   *Saccharomyces* species multiply asexually by a vegetative method called budding. Under favourable conditions, budding take place. At the time of budding, a small portion of cell wall at or near one pole of the cell softens and becomes thin. The protoplasm covered by a thin membrane bulges out in the form of an outgrowth. It gradually enlarges in size and is known as the bud. The nucleus of the parent cell divides and with it the vacuole. Mitotic division is intranuclear, i.e., the nuclear membrane remains intact during division. One of the daughter nuclei with its vacuole moves into the enlarging bud. The bud grows and becomes constricted at the base. A cross wall is formed to separate the bud. After the separation of the daughter cell, a scar remains on the mother cell. The detached bud grows and again starts budding. A new bud arises on the surface of the parent cell at the opposite end and not from the same area. In the presence of abundant food supply, the budding is rapid that the bud often produces new buds before separation from the mother cell. This process is repeated. This results in the formation of branched and unbranched chains of cells constituting the pseudomycelium. The cells in the chain or pseudomycelium are loosely joined together (Figure 9.1 a–c).

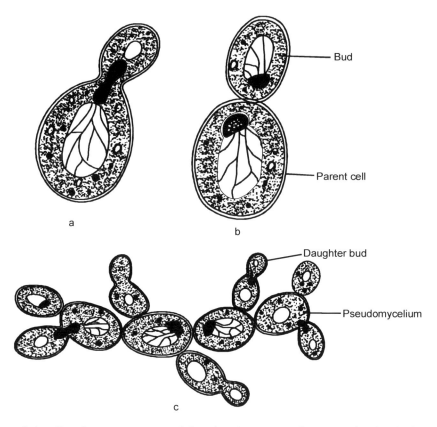

Figure 9.1 *Saccharomyces cerevisiae* showing vegetative reproduction by budding

Sexual reproduction   Sexual reproduction is by gametangial copulation. Sex organs like antheridia or oogonia are not produced. In a culture of baker's yeast, two kinds of somatic cells namely small dwarf strain and large strain cells occur intermixed.

Dwarf strain yeast cells   They are small haploid yeast cells which are spherical in shape. These haploid cells of the opposite mating types function as gametangia. During gametangial copulation, the + and – strain gametangia agglutinize to form clusters. Each gametangium secretes a sex hormone which induces the spherical gametangia (A) and (B) of the opposite strains to elongate to a pear-shaped form. There is alteration in the cell walls of the newly formed regions. The two gametangia bend towards each other and fuse to form a conjugation bridge. Plasmogamy takes place in the conjugation bridge. A large fusion cell is formed with a dikaryon.

The two nuclei of the dikaryon fuse immediately. Thus there is no dikaryotic phase. The fusion cell becomes diploid and this is called zygote.

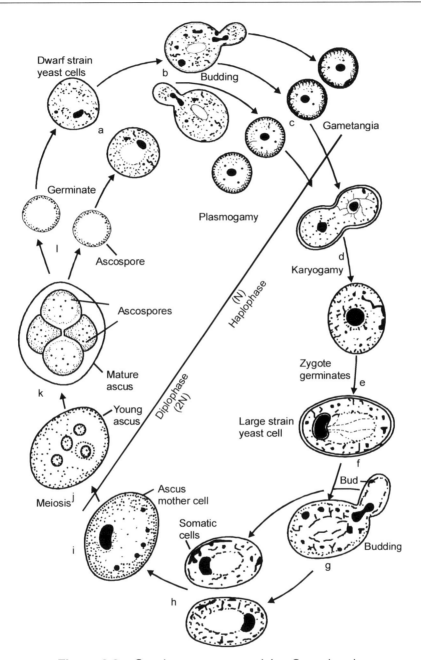

Figure 9.2 *Saccharomyces cerevisiae.* Sexual cycle

Large strain yeast cells The zygote which is formed after sexual fusion is the large strain yeast cells. They are ellipsoidal in shape. Under favourable conditions, they multiply by budding and thus increase in number. At the onset of unfavourable conditions for vegetative growth, the diploid large cells resort to ascospore formation. The cells become spherical in shape and directly function as asci (Figure 9.2).

Ascospore formation The diploid nucleus of the spherical ascus mother cell undergoes meiosis and four haploid nuclei are formed. Each nucleas is surrounded by cytoplasm and an envelope and is transformed into four globose or ovoid ascospores. Two ascospores are of + strain and two of − strain. The liberated ascospores develop into small or dwarf haploid yeast cells.

Life cycle The life cycle of *Saccharomyces cerevisiae* shows alternation of generations. The large strain yeast cells represent the diplophase or sporophytic phase. They produce haploid ascospores which develop into haploid yeast cells. These haploid dwarf strained yeast cells represent the haplophase or gametophytic phase. These cells function as gametangia and fuse to form a zygote. Thus there is regular alternation of haplo and diplophases. Both the phases are of equal importance. Thus the life cycle is called haplo-diplontic life cycle (Figure 9.3).

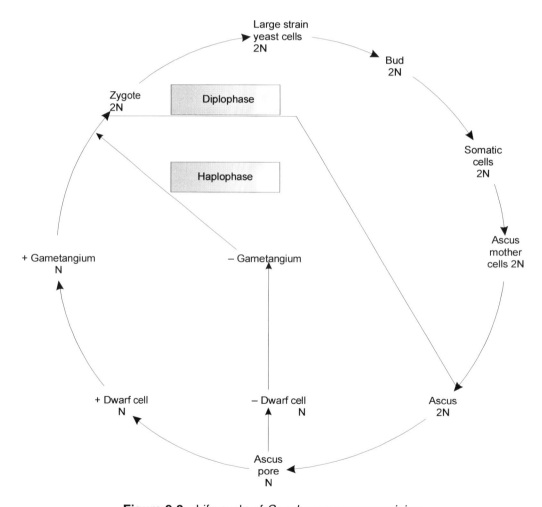

Figure 9.3 Life cycle of *Saccharomyces cerevisiae*

Economic importance of yeasts The importance of yeast to man lies in their ability to ferment carbohydrates. During respiration, the yeast cells oxidize the sugar to form simple organic compounds and releases energy. When the supply of free oxygen is restricted, the organic acid is split into carbondioxide and alcohol. These products are of immense value to the baking and brewing industries. In baking industry, carbondioxide is used for raising of dough and this gives a spongy texture to the bread. In the brewing industry, the alcohol is a valuable product. Commercial manufacture of ethyl alcohol is a large industry. CO_2 is collected, solidified and sold as dry ice.

Superior strain of yeast cells have been developed by selection and breeding. Yeast cakes are prepared on commercial scale. Commercially the yeast cakes are prepared by pressing into cubes a large number of yeast cells together with starch which is an inert substance. The yeast cakes are used in home and baking industry.

The tiny yeast cells are rich in protein and are of great nutritive value. They are grown with ammonia as a source of nitrogen and molasses as the source of carbon. The manufactured product is called food yeast. It contains 15% protein and B group of vitamins. Thus yeasts are employed in SCP(single cell protein) production.

Compressed yeast is used as a source of vitamins and of enzymes useful in the manufacture of syrups and confectionery products.

10

GENUS—PENICILLIUM

CLASS—PLECTOMYCETES

General Characteristics

The members of this class are primarily saprotic growing in soil on variety of animal and plant debris such as wood, dung and kerati naceous substrates. The mycelium is septate and extensively developed. Asexual reproduction is by conidia and conidiophores are branched or unbranched. The asci develop from the ascogenous hyphae after plasmogamy and are unitunicate. The asci are typically globose and evanescent. They are arranged irregularly within a spherical cleistothecium which is a closed ascocarp or a perithecium.

Order: Eurotiales

This order mainly includes saprophytic species such as the blue or green molds which grow on any decaying organic matter. The chief means of multiplication are the conidia which are formed in asexual reproduction. They are formed in enormous numbers and this conidial mass gives hyphal mats their characteristic colour. The ascocarp is a cleistothecium in which the globose asci are irregularly scattered. The ascal wall is evanescent and unitunicate and each ascus contains eight ascospores.

GENUS—PENICILLIUM

Penicillium species are cosmopolitan in distribution and are called green or blue moulds. They grow as saprophytes on decaying fruits and vegetables. Decaying fruits exhibit a bluish growth on them and this is due to the blue-coloured spores of *Penicillium*. *Penicillium italicum* and *Penicillium digitatum* are plant pathogens which attack citrus fruits causing soft rot disease. Some species like *Penicillium roqueforti* and *Penicillium camemberti* cause fermentation in cheese.

Penicillium can be grown artificially in the laboratory. Any moist citrus fruit or a piece of cheese is covered with a bowl and is placed in a damp warm place. Soon it becomes mouldy. Small velvety patches of blue or bluish green colour will appear on the substratum.

Systematic position

Division:	Mycota
Subdivision:	Ascomycotina
Class:	Plectomycetes
Order:	Eurotiales (Aspergillales)
Family:	Eurotiaceae (Aspergillaceae)
Genus:	*Penicillium*

Mycelium

The thallus is a mycelium and is well developed and copiously branched. It is formed of colourless, slender, tubular, branched and septate hyphae. Some hyphae penetrate into the substratum and form haustorial hyphae. The septa between the cells have each a central pore through which the protoplasm flows from cell to cell (Figure 10.1).

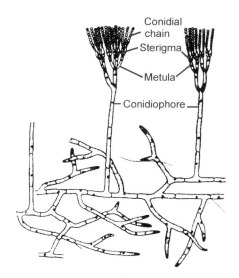

Figure 10.1 *Penicillium vermiculatum (= Talaromyces vermiculatus)*. Part of the thallus

Reproduction

Penicillium reproduces both asexually and sexually. The asexual stage however, is dominant and is the usual method of reproduction. Sexual reproduction is rare.

Asexual reproduction   It takes place by vegetative method and sporulation.

Vegetative reproduction   It occurs by fragmentation. The hyphae breakup into short segments. Each fragment grows by repeated division into a mycelium.

Sporulation   It takes place by the formation of non-motile asexual spores called conidia. The conidia are produced exogenously at the tips of long, erect special septate hyphae called the conidiophores. The conidial apparatus resembles a brush or broom and is called a *Penicillus* (Penicillium = small brush).

Conidiophore arises as an erect, tubular, hyphal outgrowth from any cell of the mycelium and is negatively geotropic. The conidiophores branch once or twice at two-third of its total length. These branches are called the primary sterigmata or rami and secondary sterigmata or metulae. The metulae finally bear the bottle-shaped sterigmata or phialides. Conidia are abstricted from the tips of the phialides in basipetal chains. The conidia are green, dry and are dispersed by air currents. The conidia are tiny, globose or ovoid in form. When it falls on a suitable substratum, it absorbs moisture and swells. It put forths a germ tube which develops into a mycelium (Figure 10.2 a–b).

In some species as *Penicillium claviforme*, the conidiophores may be aggregated together into club-shaped fructifications known as coremia.

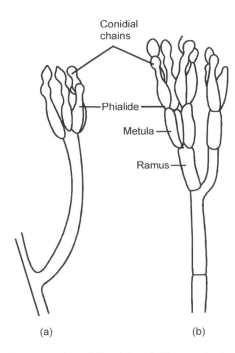

Conidial
chains

—Phialide—

Metula—

Ramus—

(a)   (b)

Figure 10.2   a–b. Conidiophores and conidia of *Penicillium spinulosum* (a) and *P. expansum* (b)

Sexual reproduction   In most species sexual reproduction does not occur. The sexual stage is called the perfect stage. Most species are homothallic except *Penicillium luteum* which is heterothallic. Most species of *Penicillium* have no ascocarps. Some species develop ascocarps in their life cycle. Ascocarps are assigned to different genera and are called the perfect stages. They are known as *Carpentales* and *Talaromyces*.

Sexual reproduction has been studied in *Penicillium vermiculatum* (*Talaromyces vermiculatus*) by Dangeard (1907). It takes place by autogamy when the female sex organ or ascogonium is functional and the antheridium, the male sex organ is non-functional. Sexual reproduction is oogamous.

The ascogonium is a long, erect, multinucleate, aseptate tubular structure. At its upper end it may be curved like the handle of an umbrella. It arises as a lateral outgrowth from any cell of the vegetative mycelium. The young ascogonium is uninucleate and the mature ascogonium is multinucleated.

The antheridium is formed at the tip of a slender elongated branch called antheridial branch. This originates from either an adjacent cell of the same hyphae which gives rise to the arcogonium or from a separate neighbouring hyphae. It coils loosely around the arcogonium to make several turns around it. The antheridium is a short, terminal, inflated, club-shaped, uninucleated structure. Plasmogamy takes place at the point of contact of antheridium with the ascogonium after the dissolution of the cross wall. According to Dangeard, the migration of the male nucleus into the ascogonium does not take place. The mere contact of the antheridium stimulates the ascogonial nuclei to arrange themselves in pairs. This pairing of the female nuclei in the ascogonium is called autogamy. Each pair is called the dikaryon.

In other species of *Penicillium*, both antheridia and ascogonia are functional. The intervening walls between the two sex organs dissolve and their protoplast come in contact. The male nucleus migrates into the ascogonium. It may divide and the nuclei pair with the nuclei of the ascogonium to form the dikaryons.

In *Penicilliun glaucum*, two short lateral hyphae arise from the mycelium close together and become coiled about each other. One is called the antheridium and the other is the ascogonium. Plasmogamy take place by gametangial contact. Dikaryons are established in the ascogonium. This is followed by the septation of the ascogonium into binucleate segments.

Post-plasmogamy changes   Septation of ascogonium takes place to form segments containing a dikaryon. One or more lateral outgrowths arise from some of the binucleate segments. Each outgrowth is called an ascogenous initial which is binuclate. Each ascogenous initial develops into a branched ascogenous hyphae composed of binucleate cells. The asci are developed by direct or indirect method of development from the tip cell of the ascogenous hyphae. Thus the binucleate cell enlarges to function as ascus mother cell. The two nuclei eventually fuse and this is karyogamy. The young ascus enlarges and diploid nucleus undergoes meiosis to form four nuclei which again divide by mitosis to form eight nuclei. A small amount of cytoplasm gathers around each nucleus to form an ascospore. Thus eight ascospores are formed by free cell formation.

Formation of ascocarp   With the development of ascogenous hyphae, a large number of sterile hyphae grow up around the sex organs. The hyphae are interwoven to form a hollow, ball-like structure. It is called the peridium which surrounds the ascogenous hyphae and the asci. This is called the ascocarp and the asci are scattered within the ascocarp. Such a close fruit body or ascocarp is called the cleistothecium.

The ascocarp of *Talaromyces* is of indefinite growth and continues to increase in size even after the ascospores begin to mature.

At maturity, the walls of the asci dissolve and the pulley-wheel shaped ascospores are liberated into the cavity of the cleistotheicium. The mature ascospores are liberated by the decay of the outer wall of the peridium. The ascospore on germination produces a germ tube which develops into a somatic mycelium (Figure 10.3 a–h).

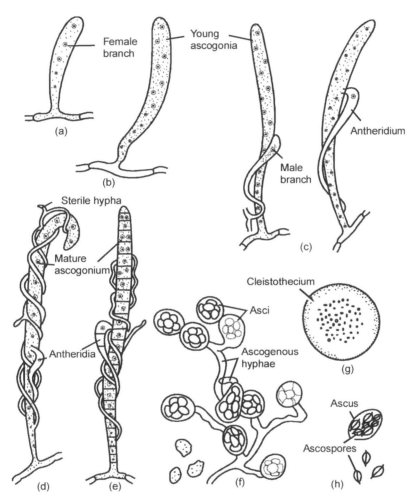

Figure 10.3 a–h. Stages in sexual reproduction of *Penicillium*. a–c—Development of male and female branches (antheridia and ascogonia), d, e— Stages in plasmogamy. The ascogonium has become multicellular with dikaryotic cells. f—Ascogenous hyphae and asci of *Talaromyces vermiculatus,* g—An entire ascocarp of *T. vermiculatus,* h—Ascus and ascospores of *T. stipitatus*

Economic importance *Penicillium notatum* and *Penicillium chrysogenum* are a source of the wonder drug penicillin. Alexander Fleming in 1929 observed that a colony of the mould *Penicillium notatum*, contaminating a bacterial culture, inhibited bacterial growth. He called this anti-microbial principle, penicillin. He used this principle in his laboratory to eliminate gram-positive contaminants from cultures. Later in 1944, Raper, Alexander and Coghill found *P. chrysogenum* to be more productive of the four types of penicillin (F, G, X and K). Penicillin G is very stable. Griseofulvin is another antibiotic produced by *P. griseofuloum*. It inhibits the growth of some other fungi and is thus used to control ringworm disease of animals and some fungal disease of plants.

Many species are important industrially in the production of organic acids such as oxalic, fumaric, gluconic and citric acids. Some species such as *P. roqueforti* and *P. camemberti* are of value in food manufacture. They are used in cheese making to which they give not only colour and soft texture but also import distinctive flavour and odour.

Penicillium species cause considerable damage to leather goods, fabries and furniture. Under damp conditions the wood of doors, windows and household furnitures gets covered with a profuse growth of the fungus which spoils the wood. During damp and warm weather, this fungus appears on bread, cheese, butter, jelly and causes spoilage of foodstuff.

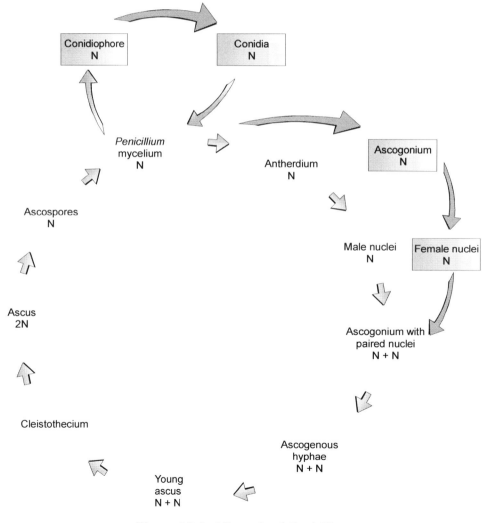

Figure 10.4   Life cycle of *Penicillium*

Some species such as *P. digitatum* and *P. expansum* attack citrus fruits or other fruits in storage.

They cause rot and decay of lemon, orange and other fruits and vegetables in transit and storage causing great losses. The fungus gains entry through bruises and wounds.

The life cycle has three phases, the haplophase, the dikaryophase and the diplophase. Haplophase and dikaryophases are represented by many stages and are prominent in the life cycle. The diplophase is transitory and is represented by the young ascus (Figure 10.4).

Genus—Aspergillus

Aspergillus is chiefly a saprophytic fungus which is widely distributed. They occur as saprophytes in soil, air, foodstuff like bread, jam, jellies, textile, leather and paper causing their deterioration. Some species are weak parasites on fruits and vegetables and some cause diseases in animals including man and the disease is called aspergillosis. A flavus may infest products as groundnut meal and dried foods and produces a carcinogenic toxin called aflatoxin. This causes liver cancer in man and poultry.

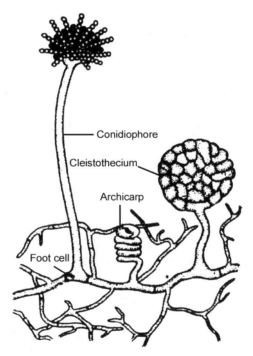

Figure 10.5 *Aspergillus* sp. A. plant consisting of a portion of mycelium bearing a conidiophore, an archicarp and cleistothecium

Vegetative structure The thallus is a mycelium. The mycelium forms a dense mat on the substrate. The hyphae are branched, hyaline, septate with uni-to multinucleate cells. Most species produce characteristic pigments which give characteristic colour to the mycelium, conidiophores and conidia. The mycelium is greenish, yellow, black or blue in colour. Under certain conditions the mycelium develops into a sclerotium (Figure 10.5).

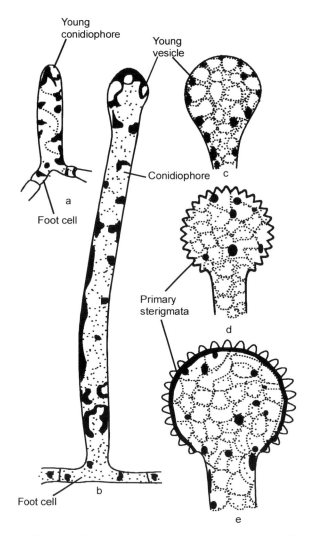

Figure 10.6 (a–e)—*Aspergillus* sp. Asexual reproduction. a—Young conidiophore arising from the foot cell; b—Older conidiophore with the tip slightly swollen to form a young vesicle; c— Older vesicle; (d–e)—Vesicle in optical section showing the development of primary sterigmata (Based on Thom and Raper)

Asexual reproduction　In addition to vegetative propagation by fragmentation, the fungus reproduces asexually by means of asexual spores called conidia which are produced exogenously in chains at the tips of conidiophores. Certain cells in the older parts of the mycelium become thick-walled. These thick-walled T-shaped cells are known as foot cells. Each foot cell produces a special erect branch and these upright branches are called the conidiophores. The conidiophore elongates and swells at its tip to form a vesicle. The vesicle may be hemispherical or clavate. Numerous nuclei and protoplasm migrate into the vesicle from the parent hypha. The vesicle is thin or thick-walled, hyaline or pigmented. From the surface of the vesicle arise numerous radially arranged tubular outgrowths. These are called the sterigmata or the phialides. The sterigmata are arranged compactly side by side and completely cover the entire surface of the vesicle. Phialides are formed either in one series (uniseriate) or in two series (biseriate). In the latter condition, the first formed series are the primary sterigmata, and those of the second series over them are secondary sterigmata. Phialide formation starts with the appearance of numerous thin areas in the thick vesicle wall. The cytoplasm pushes out to form oval, peg-like outgrowths. These are the phialides. Into each phialide migrates a single nucleus, mitochondria and other cell organelles from the vesicle. At maturity it is cut off from the vesicle by a basal septum. It is usually flask-shaped with a tapering apex. The tip of the phialide pushes out at maturity. The conidia are formed inside the tip of the phialide. The nucleus of the phialide divides by mitosis into two nuclei at the time of formation of first conidium. It is delimited by a basal septum formed just inside the mouth of the phialide apex. It secretes a wall to become a conidium. Meanwhile the tip of the sterigma immediately below the first conidium elongates to form a tube which is cut off as a uninucleate cell. It later develops into a second conidium. Thus a chain of conidia is formed at the tip of each sterigma. All the conidia in a chain are held by connectives. The conidia are formed in basipetal chains where the youngest conidium is at the base of the chain and the oldest is at the top (Figure 10.6 a–e).

As the conidial chain increases in length, the connectives begin to break down separating the conidia. The conidia are thus continually shed and new ones form below (Figure 10.7).

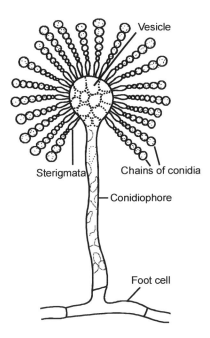

Figure 10.7 *Aspergillus.* A mature conidiophore bearing sterigmata and chains of conidia

The conidia are uninucleate at first but becomes multinucleate by successive nuclear divisions. They are black, green, blue or yellow in colour according to the species and the medium on which the fungus grows. The mature conidia are globose and unicellular. The wall of the conidium is thick and two-layered, the outer epispore and the inner endospore.

On falling on a suitable substratum, the conidium germinates by producing a germ tube which grows into a new mycelium.

Sexual reproduction Majority of the species of *Aspergillus* are homothallic. Some species like *A. heterothallius* is heterothallic. Sexual reproduction is isogamous or anisogamous. Different species of *Aspergillus* exhibit gradual degeneration of sex organs leading finally to somatogamy. In *A. nidulans* sexual reproduction is isogamous. The sex organs, antheridia and ascogonia develop as pairs of loose short coiled hyphal branches, in *A. repens*, the two sexual branches differ from each other and sexual reproduction is anisogamous. The female branch develops from a hypha, elongates and forms a coiled helix. It is unicellular and multinucleated in the beginning. But later, it divides by formation of septa into two or more cells. The terminal cell of the branch is trichogyne which is the largest cell with about 20 or more nuclei. The sub-terminal cell is the ascogonium. Meanwhile one or more slender hyphal branches, develop either from the base of the ascogonium or from a separate hypha and these are called antheridial branches. This branch cuts off a unicellular antheridium at its tip. No communication between antheridium and ascogonium has been observed. In some cases nuclei in antheridium are either absent or degenerate, if present. There is pairing between nuclei of ascogonium itself. In *A. fischeri*, antheridia do not develop at all.

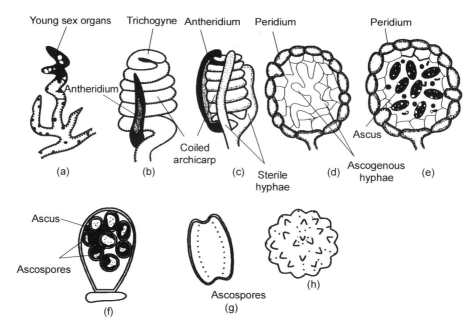

Figure 10.8 (a–h) *Aspergillus* sp. Sexual reproduction. a—Young sex organs; b—Coiled archicarp and an antheridium; c—Archicarp enclosed by sterile hyphae, arising from its base; d—Section of young cleistothecium showing ascogonium with ascogenous hyphae surrounded by peridium; e—Section of mature cleistothecium showing asci surrounded by peridium; f—A single ascus containing 8 ascospores; g—Ascospore from side view; h, Ascospore (surface view)

Development of ascocarp   Whether the antheridium is functional or not, the ascogonium develops into a fruit body which is called the ascocarp. The ascogonium has pairs of nuclei or dikaryons and after pairing, the ascogonium may become septate. The segments are binucleate. The ascogenous hyphae arise from the ascogonium and become branched. The branches are of different lengths. At the same time sterile hyphae grow up from the base of the ascogonium and invest the sexual apparatus and the ascogoenous hyphae. This forms the covering for the asci. The whole structure enclosed by the sheath is the fruit body or ascocarp. The ascocarp in *Aspergillus* is a cleistothecium. It is a small, rounded, yellow hollow ball with a smooth wall. Even at maturity it remains closed. The sheath is differentiated into a single-layered yellow peridium and one or more ill-defined inner layers constituting the tapetum. The tapetum is nutritive in function. The outer layer provides protection to the developing asci and asci are scattered within the cleistothecium.

The swollen terminal cells of the ascogenous hyphae give rise to asci. They are binucleate and directly function as ascus mother cells. Nuclear fusion or karyogamy takes place in the ascus mother cell. The young ascus represents the only diplophase in the life cycle and is transitory. Its diploid nucleus undergoes meiosis to form eight haploid nuclei. Each nucleus is surrounded by cytoplasm. A wall is secreted around this to form an ascospore. Thus the ascospores are formed by cell formation. The cytoplasm left over in the ascus is known as the epiplasm. The mature ascus may be globose, ovoid or pear-shaped. When the ascospores are formed, the ascus wall, the ascogenous hypha and the tapetum undergo degeneration to form a nutritive fluid. The peridium undergoes decay and the ascospores are finally liberated (Figure 10.8 a–h).

The ascospore is a pulley wheel-shaped structure. It is a haploid, uninucleated structure. On falling on a suitable substratum, each ascospore germinates to form a germ tube which develops into the haploid mycelium.s

The life cycle has three phases a prominent haplophase, a long dikaryotic phase and a transitory diplophase (Figure 10.9).

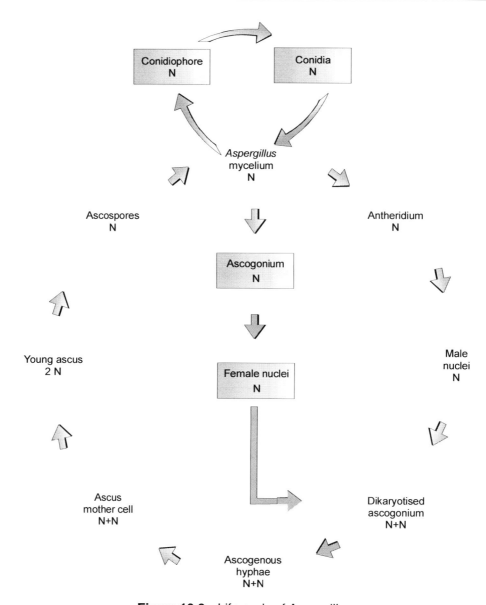

Figure 10.9   Life cycle of Aspergillus

11

CLASS—PYRENOMYCETES

GENERAL CHARACTERISTICS

The members of this class occur on a wide range of habitats as soil, dung, dead plant remains, etc. They are common on woody substrata. Mycelium is well-developed and the hyphae are septate. Asexual reproduction is by conidia. Conidiophores are either free from each other or form structures called synnemata. Ascocarps are perithecia which are usually provided with an ostiole or opening that is lined by periphyses. The perithecia occur singly or in clusters on or within a stroma. Ascocorp is surrounded by a peridial wall, containing unitunicate asci which are arranged in a hymenial layer. Ascospores are eight in number.

Order-Erysiphales

This order includes obligate ectoparasites which grow on the surface of the host plant. These fungi are known as powdery mildews because of the powdery appearance of the white conidiophores. The ascocarps are minute, closed spherical cleistothecia with a pseudo-parenchymatous peridium. They are black in colour with hyphal appendages on its surface. There is a well-defined hymenium at the base of the cleistothecial cavity.

Genus—*Erysiphe*

The genus *Erysiphe* includes about ten species. All of them are obligate ectoparasites which infect a large number of species of angiosperms particularly the cereals and grasses. They occur on the aerial parts causing powdery mildew disease. These fungi are generally epidermal cell penetrating parasites. *E. cichoracearum* causes powdery mildew of cucurbits; *E. polygoni* causes powdery mildew of peas; *E. graminis* causes powdery mildew of cereal crops such as wheat, barley, rye, oats and many of the grasses; *E. graminis stritici* on wheat and *E. graminis sp. hordei* on barley are specialized pathogens which cannot infect other genera.

Systematic position

Division:	Mycota
Subdivision:	Ascomycotina
Class:	Pyrenomycetes
Order:	Erysiphales
Family:	Erysiphaceae

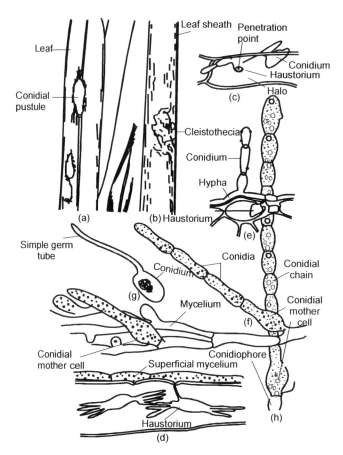

Figure 11.1 a–h. *Erysiphe.* All stages, except e (*E. polygoni*) are of *E. graminis.* a—Conidial pustule on host leaf, b—Cleistothecia on host leaf sheath, c—A germinating conidium on leaf showing penetration point surrounded by a 'halo'. A haustorium developed beneath the penetration point may be seen, d—Section of an epidermal cell showing superficial mycelium, two penetration points and two haustoria, e—T.S. of host leaf showing superficial hypha, simple haustorium and conidial chain (*E. polygoni*), f—Mycelium and conidiophores showing the swollen, flask-shaped mother cells, g—A germinating conidium, h—Conidiophore with conidial chain

Primary infection   The conidium on falling on a suitable host germinates immediately by putting out one to three germ tubes. The germ tube comes in contact with the cuticle and widens to form an appressorium with a small lobe in the centre. An infection peg arises from the appressorium and this penetrates the cuticle and epidermal cell wall and grows into the lumen of the epidermal cell where a haustorium develops. Then a secondary hypha develops from the appressorium. The development of secondary hypha is dependent on the formation of a functional haustorium. This secondary hypha grows over the surface of the infected part and branches rapidly to form the mycelium (Figure 11.1 a–d).

Mycelium   It grows over the surface of the leaf and thus is superficial. It is known as the ectomycelium. It consists of hyaline, branched septate hyphae. The hyphal walls are thin. Each hyphal colony has a single haustorium. The haustorium lies in the lumen of the epidermal cell surrounded by the host cell protoplast. The haustorium may be simple and globular or pyriform in shape. The haustorium consists of a small, slender, tube-like hypha called the stalk or haustorial neck ending in an elongated, swollen, plate-like central structure known as the haustorial body. This haustorial body bears finger-like processes at either end and lies in the vacuole region of the host cell almost filling it.

Asexual reproduction   During favourable growing season, the ectomycelium produces asexual spores known as conidia. The conidia are formed exogenously in chains at the tip of conidiophores. The conidiophores arise vertically at right angle, to the surface of the host. The conidiophore consists of a basal, flask-shaped mother cell which elongates and cuts cells in basipetal succession at the tip. Each conidial chain may have 20 or more conidia which are separated and disseminated by wind. The conidia are ellipsoidal or barrel-shaped and each conidium contains a single nucleus and several water-filled vacuoles. The wind-borne conidia germinate on landing at the suitable host and spread the fungus (Figure 11.1 e–h).

Sexual reproduction   Many species of *Erysiphe* are heterothallic. Sexual reproduction is by gametangial contact. Sex organs are formed at the tips of short erect lateral uninucleate outgrowths. These branches lie closely parallel to and more or less twisted about each other. Antheridal branches divide to form a small terminal antheridium and the lower supporting cell or stalk cell. The ascogonial branch consists of a terminal, uninucleate, slightly swollen, club-shaped ascogonium and the basal stalk cell. In the region of contact between the antheridium and ascogonium, the walls dissolve and the male nucleus migrates into the ascogonium. A dikaryon is established in the ascogonium.

Post-plasmogamy changes   The dikaryotised ascogonium elongates and divides to form 4 or 5 cells. Many ascogenous hyphae arise from the ascogonium. Ascus mother cells are formed from the cells of the ascogenous hyphae. Nuclear fusion or karyogamy occurs in the ascus mother cell and it forms the young ascus. The diploid nucleus undergoes meiosis to form eight haploid nuclei. Ascospores are formed by free cell formation. Meanwhile sterile hyphae grow up from the stalk cell of the ascogonium and form a sheath around the sexual apparatus (Figure 11.2 a–j).

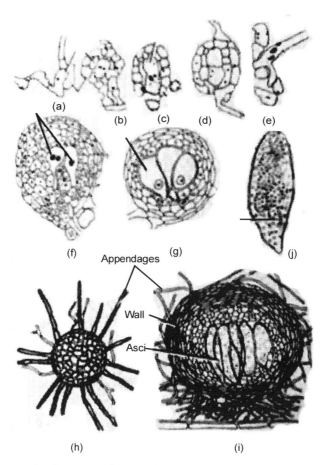

Figure 11.2 a–j. Stages in the sexual reproduction and ascocarp development in *Erysiphe*. a—Contact between pseudoascogonium (female) and pseudoantheridium (male) in *E. cichoracearum*. b—Conjugation between a cell of pseudoascogonium and pseudoantheridium. Pseudoascogonium has become dikaryotic, c—A dikaryotic cell of pseudoascogonium, d—Extension of a cell of pseudoantheridium to form receptive hypha, e—Tip of receptive hypha making contact and encircling a cell of the superficial mycelium, f—Young ascocarp showing a central group of dikaryotic cells—the centrum. g—L.S. of young ascocarp, h—A entire cleistothecium, i—L.S. of mature cleistothecium showing asci, j—A single ascus and ascospores

Cleistothecium   The cleistothecia are globose structures without an opening. They appear as black or brown specks on the surface of white mycelium. The peridium may consist of 6 to 10 cells in thickness. The cells of the outer layer are thick-walled. Certain superficial cells of the peridium develop into long hypha-like, unbranched or slightly branched appendages. The number of asci varies from 2 to 8. All the asci originate from the base of the cleistothecial cavity and spread out in a fan-shaped manner. They are ovoid or cylindrical. The number of ascospores in each ascus varies from 2 to 8. The ascospores are elliptical, unicellular, and hyaline structures (Figure 11.2 h–i).

Dehiscence of cleistothecium The mature cleistothecia remain dormant during winter. With the onset of spring, the epiplasm in the ascus undergoes a change which results in increase in the osmotic pressure within them. Asci absorb water and swell. The swelling of the contents causes an irregular rupturing of the upper portion of the peridium. The upper half is shed and the asci protrude. The exposed asci burst and release the ascospores with the sufficient force. The liberated ascospores germinate immediately on falling on a suitable host to start new infection.

Control measures Sowing resistant varieties of crop plants provides the best control of the disease. Rogueing of the diseased plants and burning them also control the disease. Dusting the crop with sulphur dust or spraying with Karathane is effective in controlling the disease.

Life cycle of *Erysiphe* The life cycle has three phases—a prominent haplophase, a long dikaryophase and a transitory diplophase (Figure 11.3).

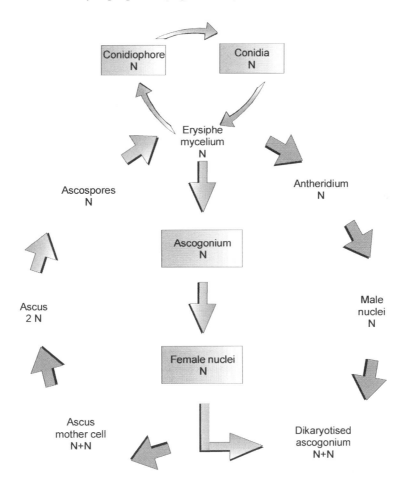

Figure 11.3 Life cycle of *Erysiphe*

Order—Sphaeriales This includes members in which the ascocarps are dark, leathery or carbonous, globose or pear-shaped, ostiolate or non-ostiolate. Asci are unitunicate and cylindrical and are intermixed with paraphyses, forming a basal hymenial layer. The ostiole is created by the growth of the paraphyses on the upper part of the ascocarp. It is papillate or elongated and is provided with periphyses.

Family—Sordariaceae It includes members which are found on dung or on decaying plant parts. These are characterized by the formation of dark, ostiolate or non-ostiolate fruiting bodies. The asci are cylindrical and intermixed with paraphyses, which are evanescent at maturity.

Systematic position

Division: Mycota

Subdivision: Ascomycotina

Class: Pyrenomycetes

Order: Sphaeriales

Family: Sordariauae

Genus: *Neurospora*

Genus——Neurospora The generic name *Neurospora* (Gr.*neuron* = nerve + *spora* = seed, spore) is derived from the characteristic ribbed ascospores. It contains 12 species which are widely distributed. The "red bread mould" or "bakery mould", *Neurospora sitophila* was discovered in 1927 by C.L. Shear and B.D. Dodge, two eminent American mycologists. It is the fungus that has been successfully used by geneticists to elucidate the laws of heredity. Thus it has become the *Drosophila* of the fungus world. They pointed out the properties that make it an almost ideal experimental organism for the study of genetic recombination and gene expression. These properties are:

 i.   The fungus has simple nutritional requirements and grows in a defined medium.
 ii. Exists in the haploid state for most of its life cycle.
 iii. Mutation can be induced by irradiation.
 iv. It is a fast growing fungus that multiplies by asexual spores.
 v.   The tetrad analysis of the spores is easy.
 vi. Its genes can be changed artificially and the role they play in the chemical alteration and metabolism of cell can be determined precisely.

Two best known species are *Neurospora crassa* and *N. sitophila*. From India, the former species is reported on fruits of papaya and from water. These two species colonize burnt ground and charred vegetables and also found in warm humid places like kilns and bakeries. It is not advisable to grow *Neurospora* in Petri dishes as it is a notorious weed of the laboratory.

Thallus The thallus is a mycelium and it grows rapidly and superficially on the substrate. The hyphae are branched coarse, pigmented and septate with multinucleate cells.

Asexual reproduction   The mycelium reproduces rapidly by conidia. Two types of conidia are formed: macroconidia and microconidia.

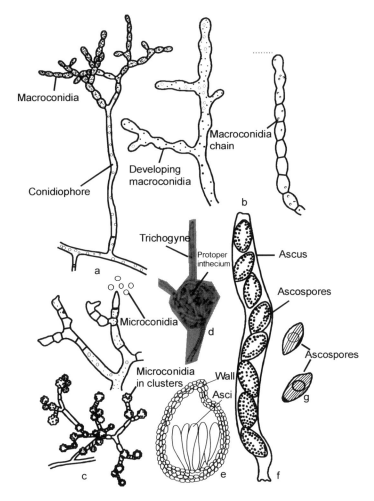

Figure 11.3   (a–g)—*Neurospora crassa*. a—Conidiophore with macroconidia, b—Macroconidial chains enlarged, c—Microconidia forming sticky clusters, d—A protoperithecium with projecting trichogyne, e—L.S. of perithecium, f— An ascus, g—Ascospores

Macroconidia   They are formed as large conidial masses on upright branches. The aerial upright branches arise from the mycelium. On each branch, there develop branched chains of multinucleate pink conidia. The terminal conidium of a chain may bud to form more conidia. Conidia of this type belong to the form, genus, *Monilia*. The individual conidia of a chain break apart, and easily disseminated by wind (Figure 11.4 a–b).

Microconidia   In contrast to the large, dry, wind dispersed microconidia, clumps of smaller, oval, sticky macroconidia also develop laterally on the upright aerial branches. The conidiogenous cells are phialides. Both types of conidia on germination, give rise to vegetative hyphae (Figure 11.4 c).

Sexual reproduction   Sexual reproduction is by spermatization. *N. crassa* and *N. sitophila* the two important species are self-sterile, and therefore, heterothallic. In these species ascocarp development does not take place on mycelium derived from a single conidium. At the time of sexual reproduction, female sex organs, ascogonia develop on the mycelium. It develops as a coiled, multinucleate, lateral outgrowth of a vegetative hypha. The ascogonium divides later. The neighbouring hyphae surround the developing ascogonium to give rise to a pseudo-parenchymatous ball-like structure of hyphae. The upper cells of the ascogonium give rise to long tapering trichogyne. The female sex organs of this type are called protoperithecia or bulbils or archicarps.

Spermatization can be brought about not only by the microconidia but also by the macroconidia and even by the conidial germ tube that can supply nuclei to the receptive trichogynes. There are no specialized male cells like spermatia. Fusion between the trichogyne and the fertilizing cell (conidium) is followed by migration of one or more nuclei from the fertilizing cell down the trichogyne into the ascogonial cell. The male nuclei reach the ascogonium and pair with the female nuclei. Ascogenous hyphae arise from the dikaryotised ascogonium and bear asci apically on characteristic croziers. The hyphae of the protoperithecium give to the peridium (Figure 11.4 d).

Ascocarp   The ascocarp is the post-fertilization product and is called a perithecium. The mature perithecia are dark-coloured, globose, flask-shaped with a neck. The canal of the neck is lined by periphysis. However, paraphyses between asci are absent. The asci are cylindrical, long and stalked. In *N. tetrasperma*, each ascus has four binucleate ascospores whereas in *N. crassa*, eight binucleate ascospores are found. The young ascus has a dikaryon. Nuclear fusion takes place in each young ascus, followed by three successive nuclear divisions during which meiosis is completed. At maturity the ascus contains eight linearly arranged nuclei. Ascospores are formed by free cell formation. Ascospores are brown to black with characteristic ridges and striations (Figure 11.4 e–f).

In *N. tetrasperma*, binucleate ascospores are produced and the two nuclei belong to the opposite mating types. On germination they produce heterokaryotic mycelium which bears perithecia.

Life cycle   Life cycle of *Neurospora sitophila* shows phases such as prominent haplophase, dikaryotic phase and a transitory diplophase (Figure 11.5).

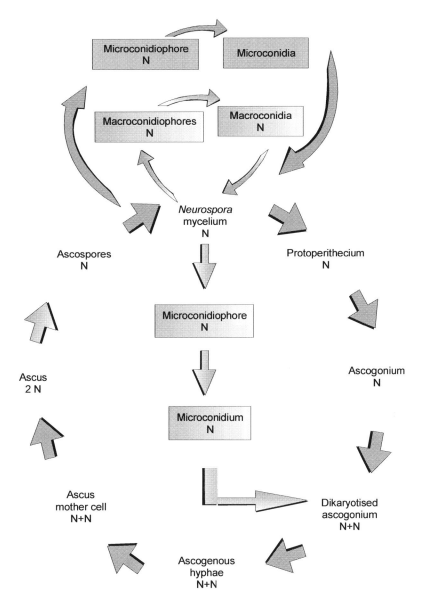

Figure 11.5 Life cycle of *Neurospora sitophila*

12

Class—Discomycetes

GENERAL CHARACTERISTICS

The fungi included in this class are called cup fungi and this includes morels and truffles. They are mostly saprophytes growing in soil, humus, dead logs and dung. Mycelium is typically ascomycetean. Conidial stages are lacking in most forms. Sexual reproduction is by somatogamy. Ascocarp is cup-shaped or saucer-shaped and is called the apothecium. Hymenium is freely exposed at maturity. Asci are club-shaped or cylindrical and are arranged in a hymenium. Asci are intermixed with paraphyses.

Order—Pezizales

Members are mostly terrestrial, growing saprophytically on soil, herbivore's dung and decaying woody materials. The fruit body is an apothecium. Asci are arranged in a hymenium and are intermixed with paraphyses. Asci are cylindrical and operculate. Asci are mostly eight-spored and ascospores are smooth or variously sculptured.

Genus—*Peziza*

It is a macroscopic cup fungi and is cosmopolitan in its distribution. About 25 species of this genus are known to occur in India. The commonly found species is *Peziza vesiculosa*. It is a saprophytic fungus and very often coprophilous in habit. It frequently grows on dung, rotting wood or humus rich soil.

Systematic position

Division:	Mycota
Subdivision:	Ascomycotina
Class:	Discomycetes
Order:	Pezizales
Family:	Pezizaceae
Genus:	*Peziza*

(a)

Figure 12.1 Apothecia of Pezizaceae. a. Apothecia of Peziza

Mycelium The mycelium is frequently perennial and consists of a dense network of branched septate hyphae. The cells are uninucleate. The hyphae ramify within the substratum and form a complex system which obtains its nutrients from the substratum.

Asexual reproduction It takes place by the formation of conidia and chlamydospores. Some species produce conidia and it is not very common. Small conidiophores develop from the mycelium. They swell at their apices into vesicles over which large number of conidia are formed. The conidia are hyaline to lightly coloured. Each conidium germinates to form a new mycelium. Some species also develop thick-walled intercalary chlamydospores either singly or in series in the mycelium. Under suitable conditions, each chlamydospore germinates and gives rise to a new mycelium.

Sexual reproduction No sex organs are formed in *Peziza*. The hyphae grow in all directions to give a pseudo-parenchymatous mass. Within this hyphal mass, there is a weft of branching filaments which is in rich in protoplasmic contents. Each cell contains one or more nuclei. There is somatogamous copulation between vegetative cells of these filaments. Nuclei in such cells then arrange themselves in pairs and form dikaryons. In some cases, dikaryotic condition is also achieved by autogamous pairing, i.e., nuclei of the same cell arrange themselves in pairs.

As a result of sexual reproduction, apothecia begin to develop. Mature apothecia are saucer-shaped, sessile or sub-sessile, 5 cm or more in diameter (Figure 12.1). Internal structure is clear in a longitudinal section of the apothecium. There may be seen three main layers. The outermost layer is hymenium and is made up of elongated cells at right angles to the surface like a palisade layer. These elongated cells are called asci and these asci are intermixed with sterile elongated slender threads called paraphyses. The middle layer is thin and consists of light coloured hyphae running parallel to the surface of the hymenium. This layer is known as hypothecium. Then, there is a third layer, the excipulum which forms the bulk or larger part of the apothecium.

The asci are elongated and eight-spored. Ascospores are obliquely placed in a row in the ascus. They are hyaline or faintly coloured, elliptical, surface smooth or coarsely reticulate. The ascospores are surrounded by epiplasm which nourishes the developing ascospores. They germinate by germ tube to form new mycelium (Figure 12.2 a–b).

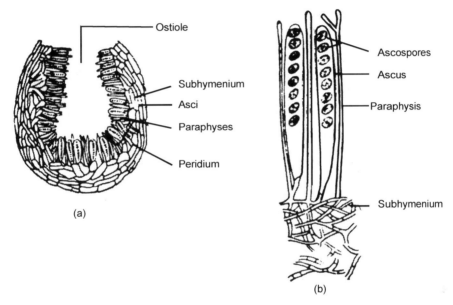

Figure 12.2 *Peziza.* (a) V.S. of entire fructification (apothecium); (b) Portion of the same to show details. (Diagrammatic)

.

13

SUBDIVISION—BASIDIOMYCOTINA

GENERAL CHARACTERISTICS

It is the most advanced and large group of fungi which includes toadstools, bracket fungi, fairy clubs, puff-balls, stink horns, earthstars, bird's nest fungi and jelly fungi. Majority of them are saprophytes causing decay of litter, wood or dung. Some cause serious wood decay in the form of rots. Some members like *Armillaria mellea* are destructive parasites destroying a wide range of woody and herbaceous plants. The commonly known rusts and smuts also belong to this group which are restricted to live tissues of plants.

Mycelium—Types and Structure

Mycelium is very well-developed. The hyphae are branched, septate spreading on or in the substratum. In parasitic form the hyphae may be intercellular with haustoria or intracellular. The cell wall is made up of chitin and glucan. The mycelium is in the form of a weft of anastomosing and interwoven hyphae. In some forms, hyphae aggregate together to form plectenchyma exhibiting varying extents of differentiation from mycelial strands or rhizomorphs. The mycelium passes through three stages before the completion of life cycle.

1. *Primary mycelium* It develops from the germination of basidiospores. Each cell is uninucleate with single haploid nucleus. The septa are simple cross walls. All the nuclei in the mycelium are identical or homokaryotic. Each segment of the mycelium is uninucleate and it is monokaryotic. It represents the haplophase. It may multiply by conidia or sometimes by oidia (Figure 13.1 a).

2. *Secondary mycelium* The mycelium arises by dikaryotisation of cells of primary mycelium. The cells of the secondary mycelium are binucleate and it represents the dikaryophase in the life cycle. There is increased prominence of dikaryophase in basidiomycotina compared to ascomycotina and this phase is independent, long-lived and thus plays a prominent role in the life cycle. Dikaryotisation of the cells of the primary mycelium is achieved in different ways.

  i. by conjugation between two basidiospores (sporidia) which is very common in smuts.

  ii. fusion between the oidia or spermatia of one primary mycelium and another primary mycelium of opposite strain. This is also known as spermatization, which is common in rusts.

  iii. fusion between cells of two opposite primary mycelia, and

  iv. Buller phenomenon.

Each cell of this dikaryotic mycelium contains two genetically distinct (compatible) nuclei. This mycelium is called secondary mycelium. The dikaryotic cell divides repeatedly by conjugate divisions. During nuclear division of the dikaryotic cell, special structures called the clamp connections are formed. The nuclei are heterokaryotic (Figure 13.1 b).

Tertiary mycelium   This mycelium is also dikaryotic. The dikaryotic mycelium which is involved in the formation of basidiocarps is designated as tertiary mycelium. The specialized complex tissues of basidiocarp are made up of this type of mycelium.

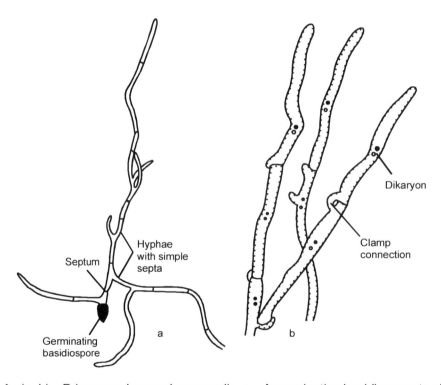

Figure 13.1   (a–b)—Primary and secondary mycelia. a—A germinating basidiospore to give primary monokaryotic mycelium, b—Secondary dikaryotic mycelium showing stages in development of clamp connections

Clamp connections   During the nuclear division of original dikaryotic cell and migration of nuclei, there develops characteristic structures on the hyphae known as clamp connections or clamps. These were first observed by Holfman in 1856. They are short hyphal branches originating at the time of mitotic division of dikaryotic nuclei. They bypass the transverse septum formed during cell division and connect the two adjacent daughter cells. When viewed laterally the bypass and transverse septum together look like a buckle or clamp. Clamp connections develop in the following manner.

When the dikaryotic cell is ready to divide, a short pouch-like backwardly directed lateral branch arises as outgrowth. In each cell, the two nuclei of the dikaryon divide simultaneously, i.e., nuclear division is conjugate. The spindle of one nucleus lies obliquely in the lateral pouch and that of the other nucleus parallel to the longitudinal axis of the cell. Two septa are laid down in such a way so as to form a terminal cell with two compatible nuclei. One nucleus remains in the lateral pouch and one in the subterminal cell. The lateral clamp curves further so that its tip comes in contact with the wall of subterminal cell. The wall between the pouch and subterminal cell dissolves and nucleus from the pouch migrates into this cell, making it dikaryotic. This process is repeated and each time an additional clamp is formed.

The clamp connection is a device which ensures that when a dikaryotic mycelium divides, each cell contains two genetically distinct nuclei. Some authors regard the clamp connections of basidiomycotina as homologous to the croziers at the tips of ascogenous hyphae of ascomycotina and have argued that basidiomycetes evolved from ascomycete ancestors (Figure 13.2 a–e).

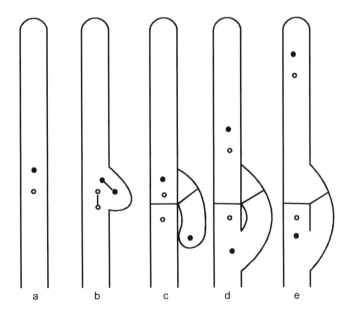

Figure 13.2 (a–e)—Diagrammatic sketch showing different stages in development of clamp connections

Structure of septum   The septa of basidiomycetes are much more complex in fine structure. Each septum is pierced by a narrow septal pore. The pore is 0.1–0.2 μm wide and surrounded by a barrel-shaped thickening, the septal swelling. This type of septum is called dolipore septum. The structure of the septum has been elucidated through electron photomicrographs of longitudinal sections of hyphae by Moore and McAlear (1962) and Bracker and Butler (1963, 1964). The septum is overarched with a perforated cap which is an extension of the endoplasmic reticulum. This cap is called parenthosome or pore cap which has several pores in it. Through these pores, organelles like mitochondria can pass (Figure 13.3).

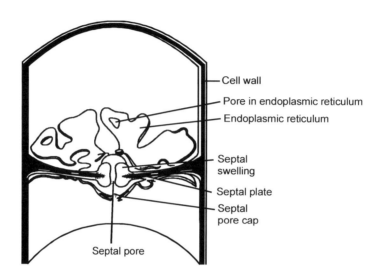

Cell wall

Pore in endoplasmic reticulum

Endoplasmic reticulum

Septal swelling

Septal plate

Septal pore cap

Septal pore

Figure 13.3 Diagrammatic sketch showing fine structure of a basidiomycete septum

Asexual reproduction   It is not common. However in some forms like Hymenomycetes, it occurs by the formation of oidia. The oidia are of two types.

1. *Wet oidia*   They are formed on monokaryotic, specialized erect oidiophores. Several oidia are formed at the tip of an oidiophore. The oidia are cylindrical, uninucleate and smooth-walled. The oidia coalesce to form a sticky globule and they are dispersed by insects, e.g., *Coprinus cinereus*.

2. *Dry oidia*   They develop usually as chains of cylindrical arthroconidia. They occur on monokaryotic mycelia of *Coprinus micaceus* and on dikaryotic mycelium of *Peniphora gigantea*. The oidia formed on dikaryotic mycelia may serve as means of asexual reproduction. However, those formed on monokaryotic mycelium normally function in spermatization during sexual reproduction. They usually germinate poorly.

Other methods are budding and fragmentation. Budding of basidiospores is common in smuts. Fragmentation of secondary mycelium is used in the preparation of inoculum in mushroom cultivation.

Sexual reproduction   True sex organs are lacking in basidiomycetes. The function of the sex organs has been taken over by the vegetative structures. The most common method of plasmogamy is somatogamy, i.e., fusion between two somatic hyphae of opposite mating types. Plasmogamy occurs early in the life history to establish dikaryotic phase. For dikaryotisation, plasmogamy may occur by the following methods.

1. *Fusion of cells of two primary mycelia* The cells of two homokaryotic, haploid, primary mycelia of opposite strains contact with each other. The wall dissolves at the point of contact and a dikaryotic cell is formed.

2. *Fusion of two basidiospores* This method is common in smut fungi. Basidiospores of smuts bud off frequently, and the buds of opposite mating type contact with each other.

3. *Fusion of an oidium and a cell of primary mycelium* Wet or dry oidia formed on monokaryotic mycelium, if happen to come in contact with a cell of primary mycelium of opposite strain and fuse with it. Plasmogamy takes place and this is followed by migration of nucleus from the oidium to establish a dikaryon. There is evidence for the chemotropic attraction of monokaryotic hyphae of *Coprinus cinereus* towards the oidium. This has been termed homing reaction.

4. *Nuclear migration* Dikaryotisation of a monokaryon by plasmogamy with a dikaryon may also occur. A dikaryon may donate a compatible nucleus to a monokaryon. The introduction of a compatible nucleus is followed by its division and migration so that eventually the majority of the cells of the original monokaryon become dikaryotic.

Buller phenomenon Buller (1931) discovered that if a homokaryon of *Coprinus cinereus* was opposed to a dikaryon, it was possible for the homokaryon to be converted to the dikaryotic state. This is known as Buller's phenomenon, after its discoverer and has been reported in a number of other bipolar and tetrapolar forms. Dikaryotisation is brought about by nuclear migration from the dikaryon into the monokaryon.

Basidiocarps In the higher basidiomycetes, the secondary mycelium develops fruiting bodies called basidiocarps. The basidiocarps are usually massive aerial sporophores which bear basidia. They are of various sizes, types, textures and forms. In texture they may be thin, crust-like, gelatinous, papery, thick and fleshy, leathery, corky, woody and spongy. In size they range from small microscopic objects to macroscopic bodies of three feet or more in diameter. In form they may be umbrella-shaped, fan-shaped or round.

Unlike the ascocarps of Ascomycotina, the plectenchymatous tissues are not well developed in the fruiting bodies of Basidiomycotina except in Gasteromycetes. Corner (1932, 1948, 1950, 1954, 1966), who studied the hyphal construction and differentiation in a number of species of Agaricales and Aphyllophorales, recognized three basic types of hyphae (Figure 13.4). These were called generative, skeletal and binding hyphae. The generative hyphae are thin-walled, branched, usually septate, with or without clamp connections. The skeletal hyphae are thick-walled have many branches and are rarely septate. The combination of hyphae used in the construction of a basidiocarp is termed the hyphal system of the fruit body. Corner recognized five principal constructional types.

   i.   Monomitic which comprises of only the generative hyphae.

   ii. Dimitic comprising of two hyphal types, generative and either skeletal or binding hyphae.

   iii. Sarcodimitic, which comprises of generative hyphae and thick-walled, very long fusiform, inflated cells whose ends taper to relatively narrow septa.

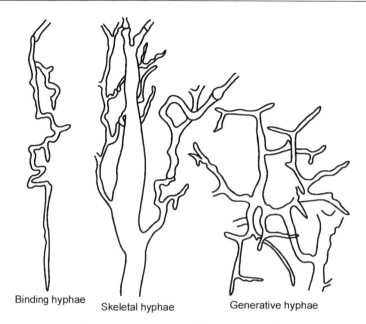

Binding hyphae Skeletal hyphae Generative hyphae

Figure 13.4 Hyphal types in Homobasidiomycetes

iv. Trimitic, with all the three types of hyphae, generative, skeletal and binding hyphae.

v. Sarcotrimitic, where generative hyphae give rise not only to inflated fusiform skeletal cells but also to narrow, thick-walled hyphae resembling binding hyphae in structure and function. The generative hyphae, in addition to participating in basidiocarp construction, give rise to basidia and to sterile structures such as cystidia, cystidioles, basidioles, setae, etc.

A special type of outer layer, the hymenium, is characterized by the parallel arrangement of the sterile elements and the presence of basidia. This covers the gills, pores or other surface. The basidiole may be a basidium which has not produced sterigmata or an immature basidium which never produces basidiospores.

Cystidioles are thin-walled, sterile elements of the hymenium about the same diameter as the basidia though they remain sterile and protrude beyond the hymenial surface. The cystidia are also sterile but frequently have a distinctive shape and occur at any surface of the basidia and sterile cells arise from a morphologically distinct tissue, the subhymenium. Any sterile tissue which separates adjacent hymenia is known as the trama.

Basidia The basidium is one of the most important characteristic structure of Basidiomycotina. If a fungus produces a basidium, it is placed in the Basidiomycotina. Basidia very considerably in structure, and the form of the basidium is an important criterion in the classification of Basidiomycotina. The basidia are of two types, the holobasidia and the phragmobasidia. The former are aseptate and thus unicellular and the latter are septate structures. The holobasidia are characteristic of most of the Basidiomycotina. They are developed in a palisade-like layer on the basidiocarp. This fertile layer is called the hymenium. The hymenial layer may be exposed from the beginning or exposed towards maturity or remains closed throughout.

Development of holobasidium   The simple club-shaped, cylindrical holo or homobasidium lacks septa and has a rounded apex. It originates as a terminal cell of a binucleate hyphae of the secondary or tertiary mycelium in the basidiocarp. It is separated from the supporting hypha by a septum. A clamp connection is generally found at the basidium over the separating septum. The young basidium increases in size and becomes broad. Karyogamy takes place to form a synkaryon in the basidium. Soon, the fusion nucleus undergoes meiosis to form four haploid nuclei. The basidium remains aseptate. This holobasidium pushes out four slender projections at its top and these are the sterigmata. The tip of each sterigma swells to form a saclike swelling, the basidiospore initial. A haploid nucleus migrates into each basidiospore initial from the basidium. The nucleus assumes vermiform shape during its passage through the narrow neck. It again becomes spherical in the spore. The protoplast of the spore secretes a new wall around it and thus the basidiospore wall is two-layered. Thus the basidiospores are borne exogenously at the tips of sterigmata. Each basidiospore has a small lateral outgrowth near the juncture with the sterigma. It is called the hilum. Of the four basidiospores two are of (+) strain and two of (–) strain (Figure 13.5 a–e).

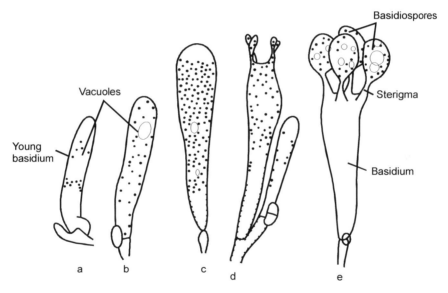

Figure 13.5   (a–e)—Stages in the development of basidium (a holobasidium). a—A young basidium with many vacuoles. Note a clamp connection at the base, b—Later stage. Note a clear apical cap, c—Localization of vacuoles towards the base, d—Development of sterigmata and spore initials, e—Fully developed basidium. Spores are full of cytoplasm.

Development of phragmobasidium   Phragmobasidium is the septate basidium and is typical of rusts and smuts. The phragmobasidia are formed by the germination of spores produced by the rounding up of the binucleate cells of the dikaryotic mycelium in smuts. These spores are thick-walled and are known as smut or brand spores. The two nuclei in the smut spore fuse to form a synkaryon. This smut spore with synkaryon is called the hypobasidium. It germinates to produce a short germ tube, the epibasidium or promycelium. The diploid nucleus undergoes meiosis to form the four nuclei and the four nuclei are uniformly distributed in the epibasidium. Septa are laid down between the nuclei to form four uninucleate cells. Each cell of the epibasidium gives out a small outgrowth or lateral projection, the sterigma. The tip of the sterigma enlarges to form the basidiospore initial. The haploid nucleus in the epibasidial cell divides mitotically into two nuclei. One nucleus migrates into the developing basidiospore and the other remains in the basidial cell. Thus each basidium produces four basidiospores. A few species lack sterigma. The basidiospores are generally unicellular, uninucleate, haploid and tiny structures.

Types of phragmobasidia   Phragmobasidia are of three types according to the division of the basidium. The division may be transverse or vertical or the basidia may have a deeply incised apex (Figure 13.6 a–e).

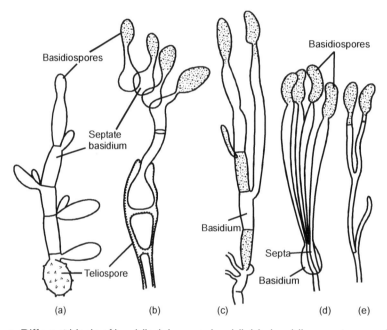

Figure 13.6   a–e. Different kinds of basidia (phragmobasidia) in basidiomycetes, a—*Ustilago avenae* (Ustilaginales), b—*Puccinia graminis* (Uredinales), c—*Auricularia auricula* (Auriclariaceae), d—*Exidia glandulosa* (Termellaceae), e—*Calocera viscosa* (Dacrymycetaceae)

i. *Stichobasidium*   The phragmobasidium is cylindric and transversely septate. Each cell produces a cylindrical outgrowth called the epibasidium. It is formed of the hypobasidium and epibasidium. The epibasidium at its tip produces a basidiospore on a short sterigma. This type is found in Auriculariales and *Ustilago*.

ii. *Chiastobasidium*   The phragmobasidium is vertically septate. Each cell of the hypobasidium is prolonged into a long slender branch at its apex and it is the epibasidium. This bears a basidiospore at its tip on a slender sterigma. This type of septum is found in Tremellales.

iii. *Tuningfork type*   In this type, the hypobasidium is borne at the end of a binucleate hypha. It is narrow and elongated with a wall thicker than the parent hypha. Its tip is prolonged into two long arms known as the epibasidia. The whole structure thus resembles a tuningfork type. Each epibasidium at its tip bears a small pointed sterigma that bears the basidiospores obliquely. This type of basidium is found in Dacrymycetaceae.

Mechanism of spore discharge   The active and passive discharge of basidiospores occur in Basidiomycotina. The basidiospores are passively discharged in class Gasteromycetes and smuts while violent discharge occurs in the class Hymenomycetes and rusts. The basidiospores which are violently discharged are called ballistospores, a term coined by Donk (Ingold, 1971). The passively discharged spores are called statismospores.

Our knowledge of the mechanism of ballistospore discharge is largely derived from the researches of Buller. The mature basidiospore is asymmetrically perched on the tip of a fine curved sterigma. The spore has a minute projection the hilar appendix, near the point of attachment with the sterigma. Just before a spore is shot out, a minute bubble limited by an aqueous film, appears at the hilar appendix, which grows in a few seconds to a certain critical size. Its expansion results in the explosive throwing off the basidiospores up to a distance of 1 mm or less. The sterigma is not noticeably altered for sometime but soon it collapses and undergoes lysis. The bubble theory envisages a surface tension mechanism. According to Ingold (1971), the surface energy available to affect the discharge is double for a water bubble as compared to the water drop. Moore (1966) suggested that the gas pressure in the bubble is utilized in launching the spore outwards. At the moment of break at the hilum, the blister or bubble, instead of bursting, simply collapses driving a jet of gas that is filled between the inner and outer walls of the spore in the region of the hilum. This propels the spores in outward direction. What is visible at the hilar appendix, for long was considered to be a water drop and the mechanism of basidiospore discharge was called water drop method. It was originally described by Buller (Figure 13.7).

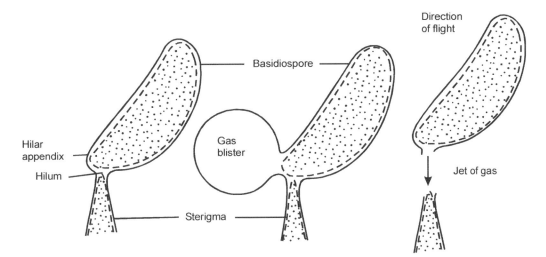

Figure 13.7   Diagrammatic representation of the possible behaviour of gas blister during basidiospore discharge (based on the idea of Moore, 1966)

The four basidiospores, as a rule, are discharged one after the other and not in one stroke. The direction of discharge of the released spore takes an outward angle from the long axis of the basidium (Ingold, 1966).

Classification   The Basidiomycotina, according to Ainsworth (1973), comprises of three classes: Teliomycetes, Hymenomycetes and Gasteromycetes. The classification is based on: (1) The presence or absence of the basidiocarp (2) Angiocarpic, hemiangiocarpic or gymnocarpic nature of the basidiocarp (3) The septate or aseptate nature of the basidia and explosive or passive discharge of the basidiospore.

Key to the classes of Basidiomycotina   A. Basidiocarp lacking, teliospores grouped in sori or scattered within the host tissue: parasitic on vascular plants—Teliomycetes

AA. Basidiocarp usually well-developed; basidia typically organized in a hymeneium; saprobic or rarely parasitic.

B. Basidiocarp typically gymnocarpous or hemiangiocarpous; Basidia phragmobasidia or holobasidia; basidiospores ballistospores—Hymenomycetes.

BB. Basidiocarp typically angiocarpous; basidia hobobasidia; Basidiospores not ballistospores—Gastromycetes.

14

CLASS—TELIOMYCETES

GENERAL CHARACTERISTICS

Two important groups of plant pathogens, the smut fungi and the rust fungi belong to this class Teliomycetes. The important characteristic features of this groups are,

1. mycelial hyphae are septate, the septa are of simple type.
2. asexual reproduction is uncommon, through dikaryotic spores of conidial nature are produced in rusts. In smut fungi, haploid sporidia may bud off into daughter cells.
3. basidiocarps absent.
4. thick-walled teliospores (within which karyogamy takes place) and a promycelium giving rise to four or more sporidia are regarded equivalent to basidia.

ORDER—UREDINALES (RUSTS)

The members of this order are popularly known as rust fungi due to this characteristic reddish-brown colour of some of their spores. They are ecolologically biotrophic parasites on green plants ranging from the ferns and conifers to most of the angiospermic plants. In recent years, rusts have been grown in tissue and axenic cultures.

The main characteristics of the rusts are:

1. dikaryotic mycelium in the host tissues is branched, septate; septa simple, intercellular, forming generally distinct haustoria.
2. teliospore on germination produces the promycelium, which produces typically four basidia.
3. many of them form several kinds of spores in their life cycle.
4. life cycles are complex which in many species are completed on two different hosts, usually quite unrelated to each other.

Genus—*Puccinia*

This genus includes about 3000 species. Of these 147 have been reported from India. They cause rust diseases in several plants, wild as well as cultivated. One well known species of *Puccinia* is *P. graminis*, the cause of black/stem rust of cereals and grasses. The common cereal host is wheat, though also occurs on oat, barley and rye. Three species of *Puccinia* which occur on wheat alone are *P. graminis tritia*, *P. recondita* and *P. striiformis*. All the three rust fungi are known to occur on wheat in India. These three species are macrocyclic heteroecious rusts. They complete their life cycle on two unrelated hosts. Many species of *Puccinia* are autoecious which complete their entire life cycle on single host species. *P. punctiformis* is an example of autoecious rust. The life cycle of *P. graminis* is thoroughly investigated and this will be taken as a type here.

Puccinia graminis   *P. graminis* spp. *tritici* is a heteroecious parasite. It causes the "black stem rust" of wheat in all wheat growing areas of the world. Till recently it had been considered strictly obligate in its parasitism. However, Williams *et al.* (1966) and Bushnell (1976) have successfully grown this parasite on culture media as a facultative saprophyte. This fungus completes its life cycle in two hosts and thus is an example of a heteroccious parasite. The wheat plant on which the fungus passes its dikaryophase is called primary host and the barberry is called the secondary or alternate host in which the haplophase is seen. The fungus can survive in the absence of alternate host. However, it can produce new races by hybridization only on barberry.

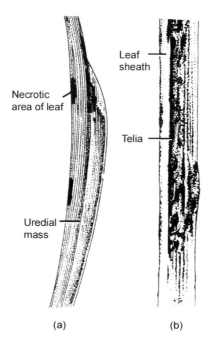

(a)   (b)

Figure 14.1   (a–b)—Symptoms of *Puccinia graminis tritici* produced on wheat. a. Leaf showing uredinia as reddish-brown powdery mass, b. Leaf sheath showing telia as black raised pustules

Symptoms Its symptoms on wheat are seen in the form of large, elongated, brown pustules on the stem leaf-sheath and lamina. These brown pustules (uredineal stage) change into black-coloured large pustules of telia. These pustules provide rusty appearance to the infected region (Figure 14.1).

Vegetative structure The thallus is a mycelium and the mycelium is dikaryotic in wheat and monokaryotic in barberry. The hyphae are branched, septate, intercellular with special haustorium. The septa are simple. Haustoria are surrounded by a distinct encapsulation (may be metabolites of fungal or host origin), and not by the host plasmalemma. They do not lie freely in the host cytoplasm. Haustoria are often closely appressed to the host cell nucleus which may sooner or later break down.

Life cycle *Puccinia graminis* is a typical macrocyclic, heteroecious rust. Rust fungi are pleomorphic, i.e., produce more than one type of spores. The life cycle consists of five spores stages and these spore stages are designated by roman numerals in addition to their specific names. These are the following:

Stage 0	Pycnidium, bearing spermatia and receptive hyphae.
Stage I	Aecium, bearing aeciospores.
Stage II	Uredinium, bearing uridiniospores.
Stage III	Telium, bearing teliospores.
Stage IV	Basidia, bearing basidiospores.

Spore forms 0 and I occur on barberry and spore forms II, III and IV occur on wheat.

On wheat The following spore stages of the fungus are found on wheat.

i. *Uredinia and urediniospores (spore form II)* The fungus produces characteristic elongated, brick red pustules, uredinia, between the veins of leaves. The uredinia are mainly distributed on the internodes and leaf sheaths. Each uredinium contains one-celled, stalked spores, the urediniospores which burst through the host epidermis. The urediniospores are dikaryotic and arise from a dikaryotic mycelium which is intercellular, forming spherical haustoria in the host cells.

Urediniospores are stalked, one-celled, oval and dikaryotic, appearing rusty red in mass. The wall is probably three-layered, the outermost being faintly echinulate. Near the middle of the spore, the wall has generally four equatorial thin areas, the germ pores. The urediniospores are detached by wind. When they come in contact with fresh wheat leaves, they germinate upon them. Each spore produces a germ tube which swells to form the appressorium. A peg-like outgrowth arising from the appressorium usually penetrates through the stoma. Beneath the stoma, the peg expands to form a sub-stomatal vesicle. From the vesicle hyphal branches develop to give rise to mycelium and haustoria. Within about one to three weeks of infection, a new generation of urediniospores is formed. A single uredinium may contain approximately 50,000 to 4,00,000 spores and there may be four to five generation of urediniospores in the growing season of wheat. Urediniospores serve as "repeating spores" or conidia.

For the development of successive generation of urediniospores, the dikaryotic hyphae become aggregated as hyphal masses beneath the epidermis. From this mass, a layer of cells arise vertically. Each cell (spore mother cell) divides into a lower foot cell and an upper cell. The upper cell divides again into two cells, of which the lower elongates to form the stalk and the upper becomes oval to form the body of the urediniospore (Figure 14.2 a–c).

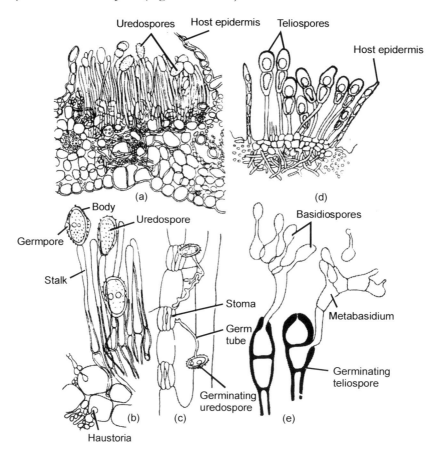

Figure 14.2   (a–e)—Stages in life cycle of *Puccinia graminis tritici*. a—T.S. wheat leaf through a uredinium, b—Enlarged view of urediniospores to show germ pores, c—Two urediniospores germinating on wheat leaf. Germ tubes over stomata may be seen, d—T.S. leaf sheath through telium. e—Germination of teliospores. One basidiospore is giving rise to a secondary spore (through budding)

ii. *Telia and teliospores (spore form III)*   The teliospores develop later in the season, which may be seen along with the urediniospores. These spores are stalked, thick-walled and two-celled. They are called teliospores. The pustules containing them are called telia, which appear as black raised streaks along leaf sheaths and stems of infected plants. The teliospore wall is thick and smooth. There is a single germpore in the wall of each cell. The germpore in the upper cell of the spore is at the apex, whereas in the lower cell a little below tht septum. Each cell of the teliospore has dikaryon.

The teliospores exert pressure on the overlying epidermis, which is finally ruptured and spores are exposed. These spores survive on straw and stubble of the harvested crop in dormant stage.

They would germinate only when the conditions like atmospheric humidity, temperature and substrate moisture are favourable (Figure 14.2 b).

iii. *Basidia and basidiospores (spore form IV)*   Under favourable conditions, teliospores germinate *in situ*. Each cell develops a curved epibasidium. During maturation, karyogamy takes place in the teliospore. The two nuclei in each of teliospore fuse to form a diploid nucleus. Diploid nucleus of each cell of teliospore divides meiotically to give four haploid nuclei which migrate into the epibasidium. Septa are laid down and epibasidium becomes four-celled, each cell containing a haploid nucleus. Each cell of the epibasidium produces a single basidiospore on a sterigma. Out of the four basidiospores developed on each basidium, two belong to (+) strain and two belong to (–) strain. The basidiospores are projected from the basidium, but are incapable of infecting wheat. The basidiospores remain viable only for a few days. They perish if the suitable alternate host is not available.

Basidiospores are small, ellipsoid, elongate, unicellular, uninucleate and haploid. When they come in contact with barberry leaf, they germinate on it (Figure 14.2 c).

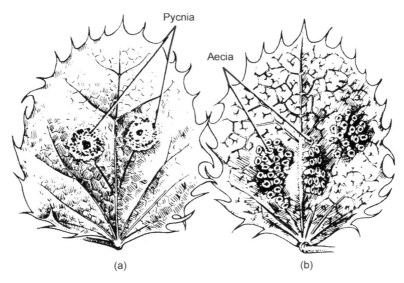

Figure 14.3 a–b. *Puccinia graminis tritici*. a—upper surface of barberry leaf showing pycnial pustules, b—lower side of barberry leaf showing aecia

On barberry   The basidiospore germinates on leaf surface of barberry in the presence of dew or thin film of water by putting forth germ tubes. The germ tube penetrates through the cuticle and epidermis of leaf. Inside the host tissue, it develops into a haploid, intercellular mycelium (Figure 14.3 a–b).

iv. *Pycnia and pycniospores (spore form 0)*   Within the barberry leaf, haploid mycelia of opposite strain (+) and (–) develop as a result of germination of (+) and (–) types of basidiospores. Pseudo-parenchymatous masses are formed by the aggregation of haploid mycelia beneath the leaf epidermis. Within a few days of infection, several, yellowish, flask-shaped structures, the pycnia develop in the upper surface of the leaf, penetrating the epidermis.

The pycnia are otherwise called spermagonia. Pycnia are small, flask-shaped structures and are of (+) or (–) strain. This depends on the haploid mycelium from which the pycnium develops. When the pycnia mature, the infected areas become swollen and are seen as orange yellow bumps on the upper surface of the leaf. They are sub-epidermal in position. They are buried in the mesophyll tissue.

Each pycnium consists of a wall surrounding a cavity. It opens on the upper surface of the host leaf through a small pore called an ostiole. From the wall of the pycnium arises three kinds of hyphae.

i. Pycniophores   Numerous fine, elongated, uninucleate cells or short hyphae arise from the cells of the wall. They project into the cavity of the pycnium and are called pycniophores. They are closely packed and arranged in a palisadelike layer lining the cavity. Each pycniophore by successive divisions of its nucleus cuts at its free tip a number of small cells one after the other. These are called the spermatia or pycniospores. Each spermatium has a single nucleus and very little cytoplasm. The mature spermatia fall into the pycnial cavity. They are non-motile and cannot infect either host.

ii. Periphysis   They are long, delicate, sterile hyphae which develop near the ostiole from the pycnial wall. At first all the periphyses converge towards a central point. From there they curve upwards in a cluster towards the ostiole. Finally they project through and beyond the ostiole end.

iii. Flexuous or receptive hyphae   Adjacent to the ostiole and below or among the tapering paraphyses, develop another kind of hyphae. They are slender, delicate, cylindrical with blunt free tips. These are named the receptive or flexuous hyphae. They are septate and may be simple or branched. Each septum has a central pore.

Spermatia function as male gametes. The receptive or flexuous hyphae function as trichogyne hyphae. The receptive hyphae develop late and spermatised by the spermatia of opposite strains.

The mechanism of plasmogamy is known as spermatization. The mature spermatia exude from the ostiole of spermagonium in a drop of sticky, thick liquid called nectar. The nectar with its scent and sugary content attracts the insects particularly the flies, to the leaf. The spermatia stick to the legs and proboscis of the visiting insects and these are dispersed from leaf to leaf or from one spermagonium to another on the same leaf. By the time the nectar exudes, the receptive hyphae grow out through the ostiole into the nectar. These are spermatised by spermatia of opposite strain. The spermatial nucleus passes into the receptive hypha and it moves downwards through the pores in the septa. Finally the spermatial nucleus reaches the basal cell of the receptive hypha which comes to possess two nuclei. This pair of nuclei is called a dikaryon. Thus the basal cells of one or more receptive hyphae become dikaryotised (Figure 14.4 a).

Aecia and aeciospores (spores from I)   These develop on the lower surface of barberry leaves from the same mycelium which had formed pycnia on the upper surface. Within about 3–4 days after spermatiation, dikaryotic cells become visible which forms the roof of the protoaecium. The dikaryotic cells of the basal layer are called the aecial mother cells. They divide producing alternately aecidiospores and intercalary cells. The aecial mother cells produce chains of the cells which are also dikaryotic. These chains are made up of alternately long and short cells. The longer cells enlarge and become aeciospores. Short cells become crushed and flattened as the spore chain develops.

In the meanwhile the marginal cells at the base of the young aecium divide repeatedly to form a wall which completely surrounds the cells in the aecium. The wall is called the peridium. As the aecia mature, the chain of the cells grow up. As a result of this pressure is exerted from within. At first the overlying lower epidermis ruptures and then the aecium splits open to form a cup-like structure. The aecial cup is partly within the leaf tissue and partly projects above it. The torn roof of the peridium often forms a lip around the edge of the aecial cup. By this time the intercalary cells are disorganized. The aeciospores in the chains become separated from each other and fill up the aecial cup. The aeciospores filling the cup are now exposed. They are, at first, polyhedral, thin-walled, unicellular binucleate structures which are orange-coloured. The polyhedral spores absorb water, round off suddenly and are jerked out of the aecium to be disseminated by the wind. The aeciospores are unable to germinate on the host on which they are produced. They can germinate only on wheat leaves infecting them. Shortly after the infection, uredia develop on wheat leaves (Figure 14.4 b–c).

Life cycle of Puccinia   The life cycle exhibits alternation of generations. These are two distinct phases in the life cycle. One is the dikaryophase which is confined to the wheat plant. The other is the haplophase or monokaryotic phase which is restricted to barberry, the alternate host. The dikaryophase is initiated by the germination of aeciospores on wheat and multiplied by the formation of urediospores and later the binucleate teliospores. Karyogamy and meiosis occur in the ripe teliospore and this gives rise to the haploid basidiospores. They germinate on the leaves of the alternate host to produce the haplomycelium. This produces the spermagonia and spermatia and the aecia. The aecidiospores are formed in the aecia which germinate on wheat plants establishing the dikaryophase.

The life cycle is macrocyclic and it consists of five spore stages.

Control measures   The disease can be controlled by the eradication of the alternate host. In the case of short cycle rusts, the following measures can be adopted.

1. Rust resistant varieties can be grown.
2. Rotation of the crop can be used.
3. The infected remains of wheat plants carrying the uredia can be destroyed.
4. Early maturing varieties of wheat can be grown.
5. Light irrigation at proper intervals will reduce the incidence of infection.
6. Fungicides like finely powdered sulphur dust can be used at an interval of ten days on the infected plants.

Physiologic specialization in Puccinia graminis   *Puccinia graminis* shows very high degree of specialized parasitism. A given strain of *P. graminis* shows different degrees of infection on different cereals and grasses. Different cereals and grasses react in different ways to a given strain of *P. graminis* and, on the basis of host susceptibility, it is possible to classify *P. graminis* into six host-specific forms or *formae speciales*, also designated as varieties.

1. *P. g.f.*sp . *tritici* on wheat.
2. *P. g.f.*sp . *avenae* on oats and wild grasses.

3. *P. g .f.*sp . *secalis* on rye and wild grasses.

4. *P. g .f.*sp . *agrostidis* on Agrostis.

5. *P. g .f.*sp . *poae* on poa.

6. *P. g .f.*sp . *airae* on aira.

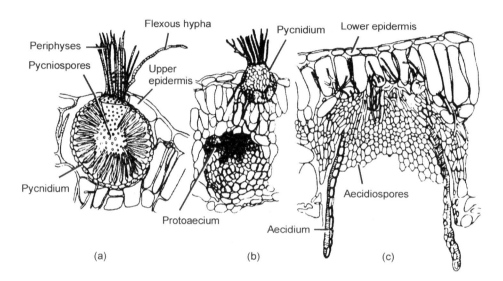

Figure 14.4   a–c. *Puccinia graminis tritici*. a—T.S. barberry leaf through pycnidium, b—T.S. barberry leaf showing a pycnidium and a protoaecium which has been dikaryotised, c—T.S. barberry leaf showing an aecium in section

Thus each *formae specialis* (or variety) specializes on its own host or group of hosts. *P. graminis tritici*, basides wheat occurs on barley, rye and wild grasses and *P. g. secalis* besides rye occurs on barely also. These resemble with each other in respect of the shape and structure of spores but differ from each other in the size of spores. A given variety can attack several species of one genus of *graminae*, but it cannot attack the members of other genera. Another specialization is shown by physiologic races in a given variety. Within variety of the rust fungus, further specialization is found. If the spores of a strain of *P. graminis tritici* are inoculated on a range of wheat varieties, these hosts will differ in their response to the infection. Some may be resistant, others highly susceptible, while yet others may be intermediate in their reaction. Thus, a variety, in turn, may contain several physiologic races which differ from each other principally in their ability to attack varieties within a host species.

Life cycle   The life cycle of *Puccinia graminis* shows alternation of generations. There are two distinct phases in the life cycle. One is the dikaryophase confined to the wheat plant and the other is the haplophase passed on the alternate host (Barberry). The dikaryophase is represented by the uredospores, teleutospores. The haplophase is represented by the pycniospores and aecidiospores. The germinating teleutospore represents the only diplophase. Thus the life cycle is triphasic (Figure 14.5).

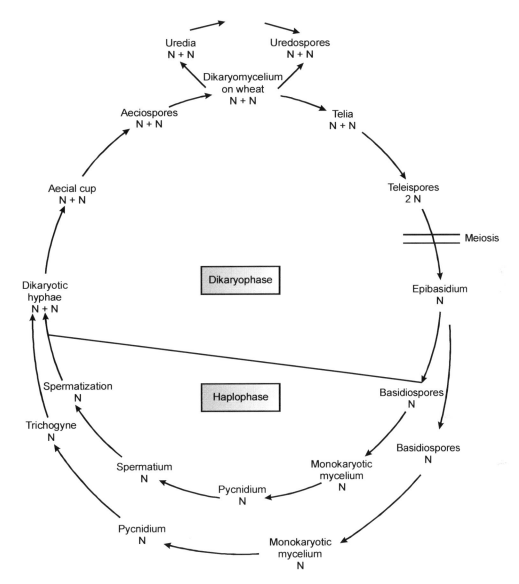

Figure 14.5 Life cycle of *Puccinia graminis tritici*

15

CLASS—HYMENOMYCETES

GENERAL CHARACTERISTICS

This group includes mushrooms, bracket fungi, toad stools and jelly fungi. Most of them are saprophytes and some are wood-destroying fungi. The basidiocarps are borne on rhizomorphs of the secondary mycelium. Basidiocarps are usually large and conspicuous. Basidium is simple, unseptate and club-shaped and the basidia are arranged in a palisadelike manner to form the hymenium. Hymenium is fully exposed at maturity. Basidium produces two to four basidiospores exogenously at the tips of sterigmata.

ORDER—AGARICALES

The fungi belonging to this order are termed gill fungi which include the mushrooms and toadstools. The mycelium is subterranean and perennial. Sometimes the hyphae become aggregated into mycelial strands or rhizomorphs. Sexual reproduction is usually by somatogamy. Basidiocarps are fleshy with monomictic type of construction. Hymenia are organized into gills.

Genus—*Agaricus* (Psalliota)

Psalliota is the generic name used for *Agaricus* in old literature. The best-known species are *A. campestris*, the field mushroom and *A. bisporus*, the cultivated mushroom. *A. bisporus* is commonly known as the white mushrooms and the paddy straw mushroom in the tropics. In nature *Agaricus* grows as a saprophyte on the ground in the fields and lawns, logs and manure heaps, etc. About 17 species have been reported from India. It grows best in moist shade and is seen commonly during the rainy season in the wild state.

Vegetative structure   The primary mycelium is produced by the germination of basidiospore. It is haploid and short-lived. The hyphae are septate. It soon gets transformed into dikaryotic secondary mycelium which perennates in the soil or substratum for a long time. Dikaryotisation is bought about by hyphal fusion. Individual hyphae become aggregated into mycelial strands. The mycelium is branched and septate, each cell with a pair of haploid nuclei of opposite mating types (dikaryon).

Fairy rings   *Agaricus* species are responsible for the production of fairy rings in grass. The dikaryotic hyphae interlace and twist to form thick, white hyphal cords called the rhizomorphs which bear the fruiting bodies. In many mushrooms, the fructifications develop at the tips of the hyphae of the circular colony forming a ring. This process is repeated with further growth of the hyphae so that widening circles of basidiocarps are seen. The appearance of basidiocarps in a ring from the invisible mycelium is called a "fairy ring" because of an old superstition that the mushrooms growing in a ring indicate the path of dancing fairies.

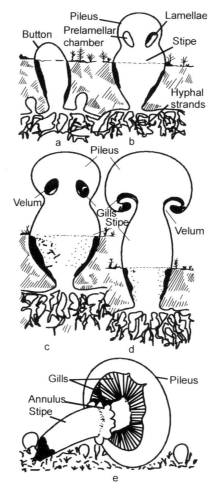

Figure 15.1   (a–e)—*Agaricus campestris*. Stages in the development of basidiocarp. a—Button stage; b—Showing the formation of prelamellar chamber in the pileus region; c—Differentiation of gills in the prelamellar chamber; d—A later stage; E—Shows rupture of velum and formation of annulus, (b–d)—vertical section of developing basidiocarp. (Based on Smith)

Asexual reproduction   It is not common. However, intercalary and terminal chlamydospores may develop. Oidia are also formed, but these are involved mainly in dikaryotisation rather than developing directly into new mycelia.

Sexual reproduction Sex organs are completely lacking. Most species are heterothallic. A bisporus is homothallic. Plasmogamy occurs by somatogamous copulation between somatic cells of haploid primary mycelia of opposite strains. Basidiospores germinate to form monokaryotic primary mycelia of opposite strains. As a result of plasmogamy, dikaryotic cell is produced, which develops into dikaryotic mycelium. This mycelium at later stage develops fruit bodies, the basidiocarps.

The dikaryotic mycelium is perennial and forms the chief food absorbing phase of the fungus. The basidiocarps are formed when the mycelium had absorbed and accumulated abundant food supply. They are developed in groups from the mycelium under suitable temperature and sufficient moisture.

Development of the basidiocarp The basidiocarps arise as tiny white apical swellings on the branches of the subterranean mycelial strands which are known as rhizomorphs. Each swelling consists of a dense knot of dikaryotic hyphae. The tiny white knots enlarge into round or ovoid structures which break through the surface. These tiny balls represent the button stage of the basidiocarp. It is differentiated into a basal part representing the stalk region and a hemispherical upper part or cup or pileus. At the junction of these is a ringlike cavity, the gill chamber. From the roof of the gill chamber grow down thin flat plates of tissue radiating outwards from the stipe. These are the gills. The margin of the button is connected with the stalk by a membrane called the partial or inner veil or velum. By further elongation of the stalk, the button projects above the soil and enlarges in size. The growth proceeds more rapidly at the upper region of the button. It is slow at the lower region. As a result the button opens into an umbrella-like cup or the pileus. At the same time the inner veil which covers the lower surface of the pileus ruptures exposing the hymenium on the gills. Remnants of the inner veil remain attached to the stipe in the form of a ring or annulus. The latter encircles the stipe close to the attachment of the pileus. The exposed young gills are white at first, but later turn pink (Figure 15.1 a–e).

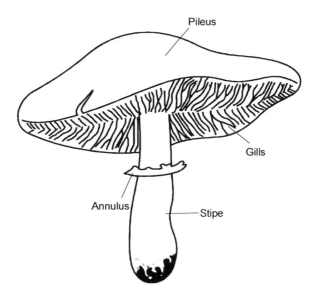

Figure 15.2 An entire mature basidiocarp of *Agaricus*

Mature basidiocarp It is a large structure which consists of a stalk-like portion, the stipe and a broad umbrella-shaped cap, the pileus. The stipe is a thick, fleshy, cylindrical structure, which is pinkish white in colour. It is swollen at the base and is centrally attached to the pileus (Figure 15.2). The stipe bears a membranous ring called the annulus. It transports the nutrients and water from the mycelium to the pileus and gills for their development. The mature pileus is 2–4 inches in diameter. It is umbrella-shaped. The upper surface of the pileus is convex, white, cream-coloured or brown. From the under surface of the pileus hang numerous thin, vertical strips or plates of tissue, the gills or lamellae. They look like partitions which hang down in a vertical position. The mature gills are dark brown or purplish black in colour. They radiate from the margin of the pileus towards the stipe. All the gills are not of the same length. The surface of the gill is covered by hymenium (Figure 15.3 a–b).

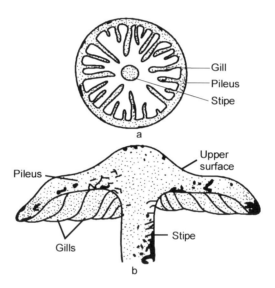

Figure 15.3 (a–b) a—T.S. Pileus of *Agaricus*; b—Pileus cut lengthwise to show gills hanging from the under-surface and radiating towards the stipe

Structure of a gill Gill is a sheet of interwoven hyphae which are closely arranged. In a transverse section, three regions can be seen.

1. *Trama* It is the innermost or central part of the gill between the two hymenial surfaces. The hyphae in this region anastomose and are irregularly woven. They run more or less longitudinally.

2. *Subhymenium or hypothecium* The hyphae from the trama give off short lateral branches. They curve outwards towards the two surfaces of the gill and form a compacted tissue of small cells which is known as the sub-hymenium.

3. *Hymenium or thecium* It is the fertile layer which covers both the sides of the gills on the surface of the sub-hymenium. It consists of a closely packed palisade-like layer of club-shaped cells which are called the basidia. The basidia are the terminal elongated cells of the hyphae of trama. They are non-septate. The basidia are intermingled with the sterile, slender hyphae called the paraphyses or cystidia. Each basidium bears four basidiospores at its free end. They are produced on the stalks called the sterigmata. The young basidium is dikaryotic. As the basidium grows, the two nuclei of the dikaryon fuse to form a diploid nucleus. It is karyogamy and this represents the short-lived diplophase. The diploid nucleus immediately undergoes meiosis to form four haploid nuclei. Four delicate peg-like outgrowths, the sterigmata, develop at the tip of the basidium and these four haploid nuclei migrate to the sterigmata. Thus the haploid basidiospores are formed and these are seated obliquely at the top of the sterigma with the spore point which is a minute projection (hilar appendix) near its attachment to the sterigma. Basidiospores are said to be discharged from basidium by water drop mechanism. When they fall on the substratum, they germinate to form primary mycelium. This mycelium soon becomes dikaryotic (Figure 15.4 a–b).

The physiology of fruit body development in *Agaricus bisporus* is known. Nutrient level and some atmospheric factors control the morphogenesis of fruit bodies. Light, carbondioxide concentration of the atmosphere/substratum, humidity and evaporation, gravity and temperature have been shown to affect the process of fruit body development.

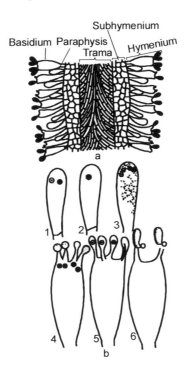

Figure 15.4 (a–e)—*Agaricus campestris*. a—Cross section of the gill showing structure, b—Stages in the development of the holobasidium

Uses of mushrooms

i. *As natural biodegraders* Increased agricultural production in our country could generate huge amount of plant residues. More than half of plant residues, mainly straw and leaves, remain unutilized and goes waste, burnt or decays. This causes environmental problems. Fortunately mushrooms have proved ideal organisms in conversion of these residues into useful products. Most agricultural and agro-industrial wastes are prone to decay, and hence can be more judiciously used for mushroom cultivation. The used compost can be used as a fuel, starting material for humus fertilizer or as a substrate in biogas plants. The widely used substrate, cereal straws, after cropping are an upgraded feed for cattle.

As a result of bioconversion of organic wastes by mushrooms, the wastes are removed and reintegrated into the ecosystem by way of natural process. It also mobilizes the indigestible lignin, cellulose and hemicellulose, the principal components of cell walls of plant residues. Thus carbon sources which are otherwise hardly usable, are transformed into utilizable protein-rich biomass.

ii. *As food*   Mushrooms are ideal food which are rich in proteins. The Indian diet is primarily cereal-based and this resulted into widespread protein malnutrition, particularly in children and women. They contain 20–35% protein (dry weight basis), which is higher than in most vegetable and fruits. Mushroom protein is rich in two essential amino acids, lysine and tryptophan, is of very good quality and supplements the cereals. Mushrooms are also good source of vitamin C and B-complex, being particularly rich in thiamine, riboflavin and niacin. Folic acid and vitamin B_{12} absent in other foods are present in mushrooms. Due to low starch/sugar content and high protein content, mushrooms are ideal food for diabetic persons. Fat content of mushroom is rich in linoleic acid, an essential fatty acid. Since they do not produce cholesterol, they are good for those suffering from hypertension, hyperacidity and constipation. Mushrooms are considered as the vegetarian meat since they are rich in high quality proteins (5–7%) and amino acids. They also contain a digestive enzyme that aids digestion.

Commercial cultivation of mushrooms   About 20 genera of mushrooms have been exploited commercially in the world. In India, however, only three genera, viz., *Agaricus*, *Volvariella* and *Pleurotus* are preferred and cultivated.

Cultivation of Agaricus bisporus   This mushroom is known as white button mushroom and is most popular. This constitutes about 80% of the mushroom cultivation in our country. It produces fruit bodies at 10–14°C, and cultivated on a selective compost especially prepared from rice or wheat straw (90%) supplemented with some nitrogenous substance. The cultivation involves the following main steps.

1. *Preparation of compost*   The compost has been traditionally prepared from rice or wheat straw and horse manure. Hay, straw and ground corn cobs may also be used. There are also efforts on the way to use bagasse, wood waste, pulverized tree bark and municipal garbage. Any such residue must undergo some decomposition, i.e., composting must occur. *Agaricus bisporus* is a mesophile. Composting is fermentation specific to mushroom cultivation. Nitrogen content of suitable compost should be 2–2.5%. Nitrogen rich supplements are added initially to activate fermentation. Potassium chloride or sulphate is also added to wheat straw. Various conditioners such as gypsum may also be added. It improves the final texture of compost. It produces a short, fibrous, well-aerated, brown-coloured compost of pH 6.5–7.5. It prevents over-compacting and improves the water retaining ability of compost.

2. *The composting process*   This process can be divided into two phases. The first occurs outside in long, narrow piles, about 1.0 m tall and 1.8 m wide. Microbial thermogenesis takes place during this phase of 7–10 days and the compost temperature may reach 70–80°C. Aerobic conditions are maintained by

turning over the compost at regular intervals. The second phase occurs inside an insulated building. The compost is packed into movable trays; 150–200 mm deep, and these are stacked one above the other with adequate air spaces in between. Peak heating occurs during this stage and this may be initiated by introducing live steam but is raised by thermophilous microbes within. The temperature is prevented from rising above 50–60°C by controlled ventilation of the room. This phase lasts 3–7 days. The purpose is to ensure controlled microbial decomposition to produce nutrients, especially proteins, necessary for the growth of mushroom mycelium. The air temperature around the compost is raised to 60–62°C for a short period. This completes pasteurization, killing any spores on the surface as well as pests such as mites, other insects and nematodes.

3. *Production of inoculum and inoculation*   At this stage, the compost would sustain rapid development of the mycelium of the cellulolytic sps. *A. bisporus* to the exclusion of all other fungi. In addition, its mycelium produces an antibiotic which represses bacteria and other fungus so that once it has colonized it is virtually a pure culture. To achieve this pure culture the compost is spawned. The production of a pure culture or spawn is another key operation in this process. Spawn is produced by growing the fungus on sterilized rye or wheat grain with added chalk to maintain alkalinity. This produces a granular spawn with sufficient reserves of nutrients in the grain to support active mycelial growth after spawning. Due to its granular nature, it becomes thoroughly mixed throughout the compost. Once spawned, the compost is transferred to controlled temperature rooms with duct ventilation to provide optimum temperature, aeration and humidity.

4. *Casing and the switch from vegetative to reproductive growth*   Heating subsides after 10–25 days, and the fungus accumulates sufficient reserves to produce fruit bodies. These are produced only if the compost is covered by a casing layer. Compost is removed to production rooms and cased. Numerous materials are used for casing. Peat mixed with granular chalk is used. The compost is covered with a thin layer (25 mm) of this mixture. This casing soil is very low in nutrients. The mycelium growing in this casing soil and compost produces volatile metabolites such as ethanol, ethyl ethanoate and carbondioxide. These accumulate in casing layer and support a highly adaptive micro flora, especially the bacterium, *Pseudomonas putida*, which triggers off fruit body production. Bacterium may make some element as iron available to mycelium for fruit body formation or may help in removing any self-inhibitory principle for formation of basidiocarps.

After casing, the environmental factors are strictly controlled. The relative humidity is maintained at 95%, air is passed over the trap at 100–250 mm^3 min^{-1} and to favour basidiocarp production, temperature is lowered to 15–17°C. The first crop of fruit bodies may be ready for 15 to 20 days after casing and the trays may crop for several months.

Proper fungicides and insecticides should be used to check infection of mushrooms.

16

ORDER—APHYLLOPHORALES

GENERAL CHARACTERISTICS

The fruit bodies are more complex compared to Agaricales, dimitic or trimitic in their organization. The development of fruit body is centrifugal with one-sided hymenophore. Veils are absent. Hymenium is not covered by a partial veil and are exposed during the maturation of basidiospores. Hymenophore is smooth, toothed or tabulate. This order includes bracket fungi or pore fungi.

Genus—Polyporus

The genus was called *Polyporus* (*poly* = much, many + *porus* = pore) because of the presence of numerous fine pores on the undersurface of the pileus. The genus contains about 50 species which are cosmopolitan mostly found on wood. All the species grow parasitically on the roots, trunks and larger branches of trees. They are common on dead or dying, standing or fallen tree trunks. Rarely do they occur on grass and other herbaceous roots. These species cause brown wood rot of various forest and shade trees and are known as the wood rotters. Some attack and destroy timber. Dalbergia, Albizzia, Oak and other timber trees are the common hosts.

Systematic position

Kingdom:	Mycota
Division:	Eumycota
Subdivision:	Basidiomycotina
Class:	Hymenomycetes
Order:	Aphyllophorales
Family:	Polyporaceae
Genus:	*Polyporus*

Vegetative structure Mycelium is conspicuous and subterranean. At first, it grows in the soil near the host roots. Eventually it attacks the roots and grows beneath the bark. The primary monokaryotic mycelium is formed by the germination of basidiospore. It consists of numerous white, slender, branched and septate hyphae. The cells of the primary mycelium are uninucleate. The cells soon become binucleate by hyphal fusions. The binucleated cells by elongation and division by clamp connections form the dikaryotic mycelium. The secondary or dikaryotic mycelium is long-lived. As the parasitism becomes more severe, the mycelium forms a complete, thick layer of hyphae around the central woody cylinder. The hyphae secrete enzymes which digest the lignified walls of the wood cells.

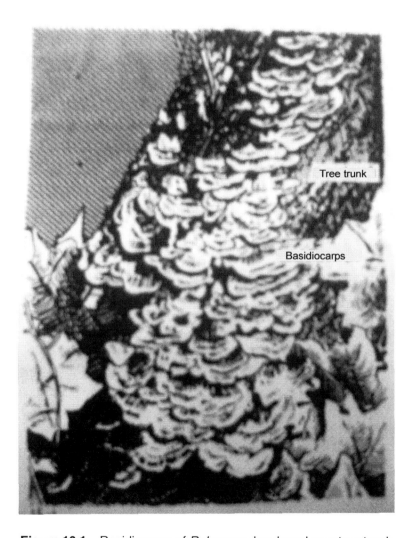

Figure 16.1 Basidiocarps of *Polyporus* developed on a tree trunk

Reproduction Asexual reproduction is uncommon. Sexual reproduction begins with somatogamous copulation between cells of opposite primary (monokaryotic) mycelia. Many species are heterothallic.

After somatogamy, there is extensive development of dikaryotic mycelium in the substrate. Under suitable conditions, fruit bodies develop on their mycelium.

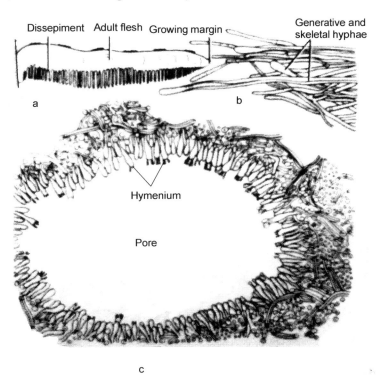

Figure 16.2 (a–c)—Detailed structure of basidiocarp of *Polyporus*; a—V.S. through sporophore, b—Group of generative and skeletal hyphae, c—T.S. across a pore to show hymenium

Structure and development of basidiocarp Basidiocarps are developed from the dikaryotic mycelium. Each basidiocarp appears as a rounded dense knot of hyphae. It arises from the subterranean mycelium. As the knot grows, it bursts through the bark. It gradually increases in size. Soon it becomes differentiated into a short stalk or the stipe terminated by a rounded cap-like structure, the pileus. At this stage the basidiocarp is soft and pliable. Towards maturity it becomes woody, corky or leathery. These basidiocarps in *Polyporus* last for a single season (annual) and constitute the only visible part of the fungus. In the wood inhabiting species they grow horizontally from the surface of the trunk.

The mature fruit bodies are generally leathery, appearing as fan-shaped brackets, sessile or stalked. The stalk may be lateral, i.e., eccentric (*P. squamosus*) or central (*P. brumalis*). The pileus is at the top of stipe. Surface of the basidiocarp may have zones of different colours in different species. On the lower surface of fruit body there are minute pores which may be round, angular or irregular in shape (Figure 16.1).

In between the upper surface of the fruit body and the tube layer, there is a sterile tissue of varying thickness. It is composed of interwoven mass of dikaryotic hyphae. There may be only generative hyphae or generative and skeletal or generative, skeletal and binding hyphae depending upon the species. Different kinds of hyphae constitute the various parts of the fruit body. These are (i) growing margin (ii) adult flesh (iii) context immediately above the tubes and (iv) dissepiments (v) the tissue separating the tubes (Figure 16.2).

Three different kinds of hyphae are present (Figure 16.3).

i. *Generative hyphae*   They are thin-walled near the growing margin, often thick walled behind with or without clamps, with distinct cytoplasmic contents.

ii. *Binding hyphae*   They are much branched, narrow, thick walled, of limited growth. They interweave with other hyphae of flesh.

iii. *Skeletal hyphae*   They are unbranched walled hyhae with a narrow lumen which arise as lateral branches of the generative hyphae.

When all the three types of hyphae are present, the fruit body is said to be trimitic. e.g., *P. versicolor*, whereas in *P. sulphureus* it is dimitic.

As revealed by the longitudinal section of the sporophore, the circular pores on the lower surface of fruit body are in fact the openings of numerous vertically placed tubes which are attached to lower surface of the context. The tubes run parallel to each other within the sporocarp. In between the tubes the tissue made up of generative and skeletal hyphae is called the dissepiment. Cross section of the tube shows the hymenium. From the hyphae dissepiment, short branches arise at right angles to the length of tube which develop into fertile club-shaped structures, basidia and sterile structures, paraphyses. Basidia are interspersed with sterile cystidia which are larger than basidia. This layer lining the pore is called the hymenium.

The young basidia are single-celled and uninucleate. At maturity the nuclear fusion takes place followed by meiosis. Sterigmata develop at the apex of basidium which bear four haploid oval basidiospores. These are discharged in the pore sac through which they pass out. Discharge of spores continues for weeks or months during which billions of spores are liberated. Basidiospores on germination develop monokaryotic mycelium.

Economic importance   The fruit bodies of *Polyporus betulinus* are used in the manufacture of charcoal crayons. In olden times the upper surface of the pileus was considered as an efficient razor strap. Some parasitic species cause diseases of forest and shade trees. A few attack and destroy timber. *P. squamosus* attacks and damages living trees of several genera and destroy structural wood. *P. betulinus* is a destructive parasite of beach, oak and other conifers. The saprophytic polypores are active agents of wood decomposition. A few soft, fleshy species are edible and sold in local markets.

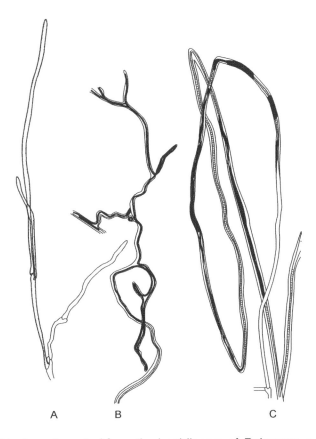

Figure 16.3 (a–c)—Hyphae dissected from the basidiocarp of *Polyporus*. a—Generative hyphae, b—Binding hyphae (branched and thick-walled). c—Skeletal hyphae

17

CLASS—GASTROMYCETES

GENERAL CHARACTERISTICS

This group is in fact an unusual assemblage of basidiomycetes in which the basidiospores are not discharged violently from the basidia. Basidiocarps are typically angiocarpous, i.e., permanently closed even at maturity. It has an outer peridium enclosing a central fertile region, the gleba. Basidiospores are symmetrically placed on the sterigmata. Generally, the basidia open into cavities within the fruit body, and basidiospores are released into these cavities.

ORDER—LYCOPERDALES

This order includes puff balls (*Lycoperdon*, *Calvatia*) and earth stars (*Geastrum*). The basidiocarps may begin to develop beneath the soil surface, but they mature above ground. The peridium wall is two-layered, the outer exo and the inner endoperidium. There is a central fertile part, called gleba.

Genus—*Lycoperdon*

Lycoperdon is popularly called the puff ball because of the method of spore dispersal and ball-shaped appearance. These species grow as saprophytes in the grassy open fields, city lawns, pastures, in the wood, on the ground, tree stumps decaying logs of wood and sawdust heaps. Fives species of this genus are known to occur in India. The two common species are *L. elongatum* and *L. atropurpureum*.

Systematic position

Kingdom:	Mycota
Division:	Eumycota
Subdivision:	Basidiomycotina
Class:	Gastromycetes
Order:	Lycoperdales

Family: Lycoperdaceae

Genus: *Lycoperdon*

Vegetative structure   The primary mycelium produced by the germination of basidiospore consists of short, uninucleate cells. It is short-lived and soon becomes transformed into a dikaryotic secondary mycelium. Dikaryotic mycelium is developed as a result of somatogamy and repeated divison of dikaryotic cells. The cells have paired nuclei. Clamp connections are absent. This mycelium aggregates as mycelial cords called rhizomorphs. The rhizomorphs have an outer cortex, made up of loosely or compactly packed mass of hyphae and a central core or medulla with parallely arranged hyphae.

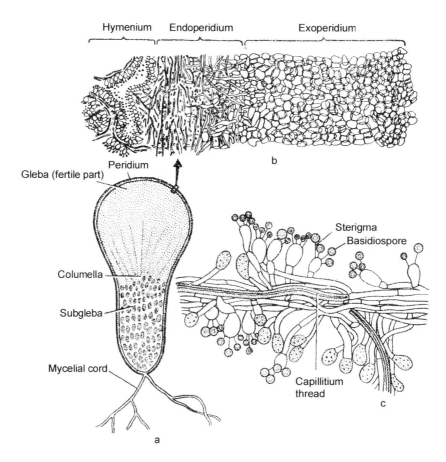

Figure 17.1 (a–c)—*Lycoperdon pyriforme*. a—L.S. basidiocarp; b—A part of the peridium and gleba; c—A part of the gleba, showing capilliitium thread, basidia and basidiospores

Structure and development of basidiocarps   Fruit bodies arise on the mycelial cords. It arises as a tiny, hyphal, knotlike outgrowth from the medulla or central core at the tip of the rhizomorphs. Occasionally it may be lateral in postion. The young basidiocarp primordium is a homogenous mass of interlaced hyphae. There is no distinction into gleba and peridium. With further growth, a palisadelike layer of closely arranged hyphae forms all over the basidiocarp primordium. Later it becomes differentiated into an outer pseudo-parenchymatous portion termed the exoperidium and the inner palisadelike endoperidium. With the differentiation of these two peridial layers around the young basidiocarp, the hyphae in the centre of the embryonic gleba begin to pull away from one another. Consequently numerous small irregular cavities are formed in the central region of the gleba. However, their formation spreads towards the periphery. Thus the gleba is of lacunose type. With the increase in the size of the cavities, club-shaped basidia are formed at the tips of the newly formed hyphal branches. These arise from the encircling hyphae which form the wall of the cavites, the cells are binucleate and these are the young basidia. The basidia are arranged in a regular fertile layer, hymenium which lines each cavity. Karyogamy takes place in the basidium which is immediately followed by meiosis to form four haploid nuclei. Four long sterigmata develop at the apex of the basidium and uninucleate basidiospores are formed singly at the tips of sterigmata. The mature basidiospores are globose in shape and have thick variously ornamented wall. The mature basidiospores fall off the basidia and completely fill the cavities. Subsequently the basidia and most of the hyphae constituting the gleba disintegrate. The remaining hyphae become thick-walled to constitute the capillitium which is intermingled with the powdery mass of spores (Figure 17.1 a–c).

Structure   The mature basidiocarp is a globular, pear-shaped or ovoid structure which may be sessile or may have a sterile, stalklike base. It consists of an outer dry sheath or jacket which encloses the sporebearing tissue called gleba. The sterile, dry, thin jacket is the endoperidium. The exoperidium withers away towards maturity. There is a small circular opening, the ostiole in the centre at the top of the endoperidium (Figure 17.2). When the basidiocarp is hit by rain drops or wind-borne debris or when any object touches the basidiocarp, the brown basidiospores are released by puffing action (Figure 17.3). The spores are intermingled with the sterile remains of branched hyphal threads of the gleba and this constitutes the capillitium.

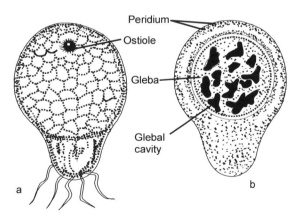

Figure 17.2   (a–c). *Lycoperdon* sp. a—Basidiocarp; b—Longitudinal section of a young basidiocarp;

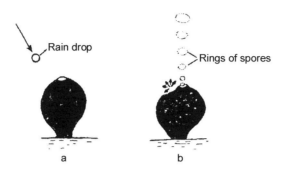

Figure 17.3 Shows how a puff ball acts like a bellows during spore release. a—before a rain drop hits the puff ball; b—after impact

Economic importance   The young puff balls of most species are edible. North American Indians hold that eating the giant puff balls prevents stomach tumours. Recent investigations have shown that Calvatia (the giant puff ball) contains an anti-cancer substance known as calvacin.

18

ORDER—NIDULARIALES

The members of Nidulariales are commonly called bird's nest fungi. The fruit bodies are globose and the fertile region gleba is differentiated into one or more spherical to lens-shaped peridioles or glebal chambers which contain the basidiospores. The common genera are *Cyathus*, *Sphearobolus* and *Crucibulum*.

Systematic position

Kingdom:	Mycota
Division:	Eumycota
Subdivision:	Basidiomycotina
Class:	Gastromycetes
Order:	Nidulariales
Family:	Nidulariaceae
Genus:	*Cyathus*

Genus—Cyathus *Cyathus* is the most beautiful among the bird's nest fungi and has 42 species (Brodic) growing in soil, wood, etc. *C. striatus* is a fairly common and widely distributed species which is usually found on rotting wood. Mature fruit bodies are funnel shaped. These develop on cereal stubbles or on old stumps and twigs or on dung. Some species can be induced to fruit on culture media (Figure 18.1).

The fruit body is initiated at the tip of a mycelial strand as a knot of hyphae. It is globose initially but later becomes funnel or vase-shaped due to the rupture of the papery epiphragm. The mature fruit body is 1.5 cm high and about 1 cm in diameter at the mouth. It is reddish brown and hairy outside; the inner surface is shining grey and marked with longitudinal striations.

About a dozen lentil-shaped, white peridioles, 2–3 mm in diameter, lie nestled inside the fruit body. The peridioles are attached to the inner peridial wall by means of a short mycelial strand called funiculus.

The wall of the peridiole is many-layered, one of which is very hard. Inside the peridiole is a cavity which, in the young stage, is lined with basidia but later, when the basidia are digested, the basidiospores lie free in the cavity (Figure 18.2).

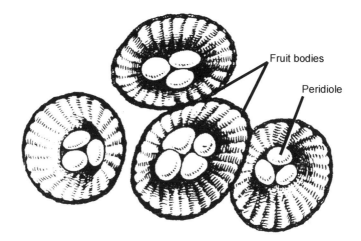

Figure 18.1 Mature fruit bodies of *Cyathus* containing peridioles

The funiculus is made up of the following components

1. **Sheath**—It is a tubular network of hyphae attached to the inner wall of peridium.
2. **Middle piece**—The innermost hyphae of the sheath unite together to form a short cordlike structure, the middlepiece.
3. **Purse**—The middle piece flares out at its top where its hyphae are attached to a cylindrical sac, the purse, which is firmly attached to the peridiole at a small depression.
4. **Funicular cord**—It is a long strand of spirally coiled hyphae folded within the purse. It is hygroscopic in nature. During wet conditions, it absorbs lot of moisture and becomes uncoiled and expanded to a length of 15 to 30 cm. During dry conditions, it looses the moisture content and becomes condensed, held within the purse.
5. **Hapteron**—The free end of the funicular cord is composed of a tangular mass of adhesive hyphae which is called hapteron.

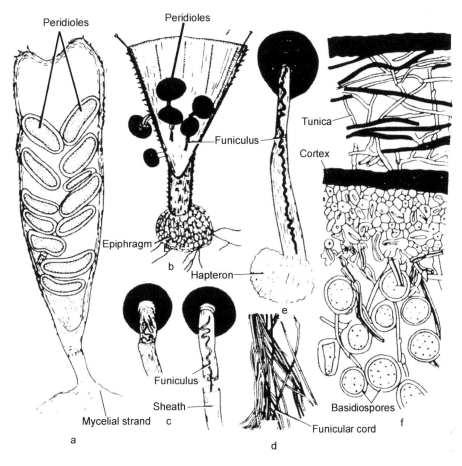

Figure 18.2 a-f. Cyathus. a—L.S. immature fruit body to show peridioles in section, b—Fruit body cut open, c–e—Details of structure of funiculus. f—Details of peridiole wall and contents.

The dissemination of peridioles is brought about by rain drops and the mechanism of discharge is called splash cup mechanism (Brodie, 1954). The mature peridioles are splashed out by the rain drops at fairly a long distance. Probably funiculus plays an important role in the mechanism of their discharge. When rain drops fall at a particular velocity (6 metre/second), the peridioles are forcibly ejected out to a distance of 3–4 feet. Due to the force, the purse opens and the spirally wound funicular cord is exposed. It absorbs the moisture content and expands to a length of 15–30 cm. Hapteron is sticky which helps in attaching the peridioles to surrounding vegetation. Peridioles of *C. stercorcus* are presumably eaten by herbivorous animals. They have long viability period which may extend up to several years. The peridioles release the basidiospores inside the alimentary canal of these herbivorous animals and the basidiospores are stimulated to germinate by incubation at about body temperature of animals (Figure 18.3).

The basidiospores germinate on rotten wood and directly give rise to dikaryotic hyphae. Some species like *C. stercoreus* is coprophilous, growing on cow dung, or horse dung or manure heaps.

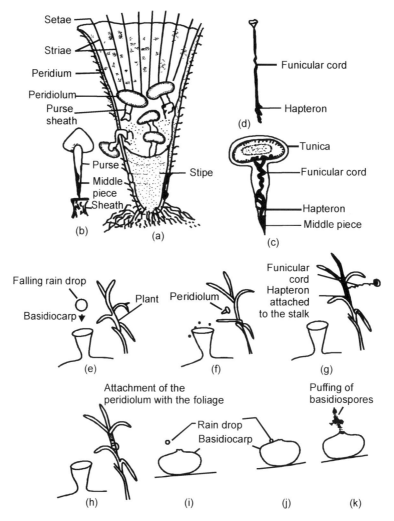

Figure 18.3 (a–g) *Cyathus striatus*. (a-d)—Structure of mature fruit body showing names of various structures. (e–h)—Diagrams to illustrate liberation of periodiole by impaction. (i–k)—*Lycoperdon*. Consequences of a rain drop falling on the outside of a peridium of a puff ball

19

SUBDIVISION—DEUTEROMYCOTINA (FUNGI IMPERFECTI)

GENERAL CHARACTERISTICS

This subdivision comprises of a group of fungi in which only the asexual or imperfect stage is known. The sexual stage or the perfect stage is not known. The perfect stage is either non-existent or has not been discovered so far. The life cycle of these forms is thus incompletely known. The advantage of sexual process in some fungi is derived by an alternative, the para-sexual cycle where recombination may occur.

Members of this group occur mostly as saprophytes on a wide range of substrates and there are large numbers of parasitic forms also causing a variety of diseases in plants. These include the common leaf spots, blights, wilt, anthracnose and rots of various kinds. In animals including man, some forms are responsible for diseases like meningitis, candidiasis, skin diseases, nail diseases, dermatomycosis as ringworm, athlete's foot, etc.

Vegetative structure   The somatic phase consists only of the haploid mycelium. The mycelium is made up of branched and septate hyphae and the cells are usually multinucleate.

Reproduction   They reproduce only by asexual methods. The most common method of reproduction is by conidia. The conidia develop in different ways.

Types of conidial development   According to Ellis (1971), the following types of conidial development can be recognized (Figure 19.1).

1. *Thallic*   There is no enlargement of recognizable conidial initial or, when such development does occur, it takes place after the initial has been delimited by a septum, e.g., *Geotrichum candidum*.

2. *Blastic*   Marked enlargement of recognizable conidial initial takes place before it is delimited by a septum.

Two types are distinguished here

a. Holoblastic   Both the outer and inner walls of a conidiogenous cell contribute towards the formation of conidia, e.g., *Stemphylium*. In *Cladosporium*, the conidial chain is branched due to formation of two buds at the apex of a conidium. If a holoblastic conidiogenous cell blows at a single point, it is monoblastic, if at several points, polyplastic as in *Aureobasidium pullulans*.

b. Enteroblastic   Only the inner wall of conidiogenous cells or neither wall contributes towards the formation of conidia. It may be of two types.

i. Tretic   The conidium develops by the protrusion of the inner wall through a channel in the outer wall. e.g., *Helminthosporium velutinum*.

ii. Phialidic   Conidia develop in basipetal succession from a specialized conidiogenous cell, the phialide. The wall of phialide does not contribute to the wall surrounding the phialoconidium. e.g., *Aspergillus* and *Penicillium*.

The conidia in general show variation in shape and colour. They may be unicellular, bicellular or multicellular. They may be globose, elliptical, ovoid, cylindrical, branched or spirally coiled. They may be hyaline, brightly coloured or dark.

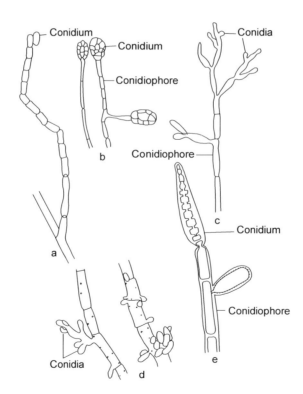

Figure 19.1   (a–e)—Types of conidial development in Deuteromycotina

Conidial fructifications   If the conidiophores are little differentiated from vegetative hyphae, they are called micronematous. Macronematous is the term used to describe well-differentiated conidiophores.

The conidiophores may occur in distinct fructifications (conidiomata). These asexual fructifications are of the following types.

1. *Synnema or coremium* In these fructifications conidiophores are aggregated to form parallel fascicles of closely appressed hyphae. The conidiophores are diverge and free at its tips. Conidia arise from the tips (Figure 19.2).

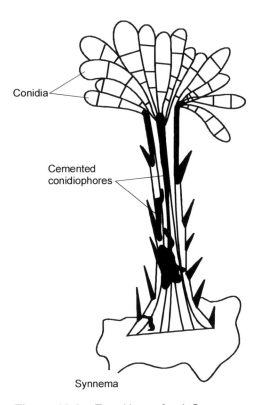

Figure 19.2 Fungi Imperfecti. Synnema

2. *Sporodochium* Sporodochium is a hemispherical or barrel-shaped asexual fructification. It consists of a lower cushioned stromalike mass of hyphae and an upper region. From the exposed upper surface the conidiophores arise which bear conidia at their tips. Thus the conidiophores constitute the upper part of the sporodochium.

3. *Acervulus* It is a pseudo-parenchymatous aggregation of hyphae which develops beneath surface of the host. It eventually forms a superficial layer of conidiophores, e.g., *Colletotrichum graminicola* (Figure 19.3).

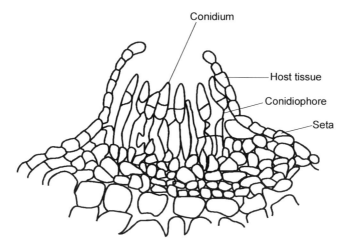

Figure 19.3 Fungi Imperfecti. Acervulus

4. *Pycnidium* It is a flask-shaped or globose fructification pycnidium surrounded by a pseudo-parenchymatous tissue called the pycnidial wall. The cavity of the pycnidium is lined by conidiogenous cells or fertile conidiophores. The conidia are abstricted from the tip of the conidiophores. The pycnidia open to the exterior by a small pore called the ostiole (Figure 19.4).

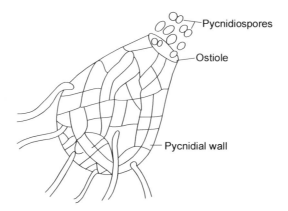

Figure 19.4 Fungi Imperfecti. Pycnidium

Classification of Deuteromycotina

The classification of Deuteromycotina is completely artificial. It is mainly based on the conditional peculiarities. It can be called a key which helps in identifying the fungi. Deuteromycotina is thus an artificial division to include fungi which do not fit in the other groups of fungi. The classification is based on

    i.   The presence or absence of conidia.

    ii.   Colour, shape and septation of conidia.

    iii.   Kind of asexual fruiting body.

Class—Blastomycetes

The class includes the imperfect yeasts which exist as budding cells or pseudo-myelium and do not form asco or basidiospores. The forms producing ballistospores (explosively discharged spores) are placed in the family **Sporobolomycetaceae** while the forms which do not produce ballistospores are placed in the family **Cryptococcauae**.

Genus—*Candida*

It is a large genus with 11 species. The yeast phase, comprising of budding cells, is dominant over the pseudo-mycelial form which is formed during inadequate nutrition or other adverse factors. Only a few species form true mycelium under rare circumstances.

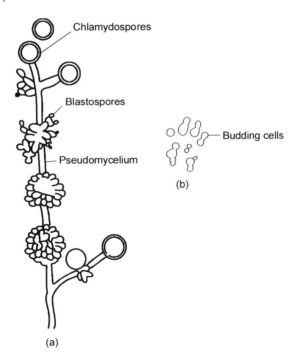

Figure 19.5 *Candida albicans.* (a)—Pseudomycelium bearing blastospores and chlamydospores; (b)—'Yeast' phase comprising of budding cells

Candida albicans is the best studied species. It was the first fungus reported to cause disease in man. The fungus causes 'thruh', an infection of mucous membranes of various parts, technically called candidiasis.

In laboratory cultures, it forms white or creamy, opaque pastelike colonies, which consist of sub-globose to oval budding cells. The cells frequently show bipolar or tetrapolar budding, i.e., buds arise from two or four places. As the colony becomes older it shows pseudomycelium or branched true mycelium bearing blastospores and chlamydospores which is a characteristic feature of this species (Figure 19.5). The mycelial stage can be induced by growing the fungus on corn-meal agar medium added with bile at 27°C. The mycelium can be visibly demonstrated by a "stab-culture".

Stab culture A beef-peptone gelatin medium is inoculated by stabbing with a needle. Creamy, butter-like colonies consisting of budding cells develop on the surface of the medium. After a few days, fine tufts of hyphae appear radiating at right angles from the line of the stab, like a fir tree. The hyphae, under the microscope show clusters of budding yeast cells and chlamydospores, both terminal and intercalary (Figure 19.6).

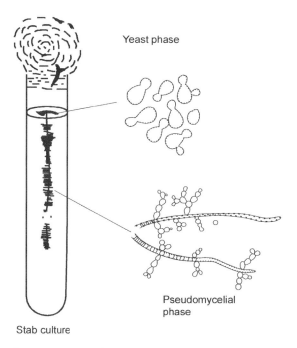

Yeast phase

Pseudomycelial phase

Stab culture

Figure 19.6 "Stab culture" of *Candida albicans*

Candidiasis The infection by *Candida albicans* is called candidiasis or 'thrush'. Superficial candidiasis affects the skin and mucous membranes. In oral thrush (an example of superficial candidiasis) the mucous membranes of mouth, tongue and palate develop soft white or creamy, curdlike patches. The white material consists of pseudomycelium and blastospores of *C. albicans* mixed with dead epithelial cells, leucocytes and particles of food. Similar inflections of the oesophagus and the intestine are called oesophagal thrush. Other examples of superficial candidiasis include ulcers on the cornea of eyes, maceration of finger clefts (more common in women engaged in washing work), infections of genitoural folds or perianal skin in both men and women.

Systemic candidiasis involves infection of the respiratory, circulatory, urinary and the central nervous system.

20

CLASS—HYPHOMYCETES

The members of Hyphomycetes form spores directly on the hyphae or on sporophores (free or aggregated) but never in pycnidia or acervuli. The forms thrive on a variety of substrata, which are mostly terrestrial. Some aquatic forms are also common.

Genus—*Cercospora*

This genus *Cercospora* includes about 3,800 species. Majority of them are plant pathogens which cause leaf spot disease of higher plants of economic value. The leaf spot disease is called the tikka disease. *C. personata* and *C. arachidicola* are the two commonly known species which cause the leaf spot (tikka) disease of groundnut (*Arachis hypogea*).

Mycelium   The mycelium in many species is entirely internal. The hyphae ramify in the intercellular spaces between the mesophyll cells of the host leaf obtaining nutrition by sending haustoria into the spongy and palisade cells. In *C. arachidicola*, the mycelium consists of both external and internal hyphae. The latter in the beginning are intercellular but later on become intracellular. They do not produce haustoria. The hyphae, when young, are hyaline but later turn brown.

Disease symptoms   In tikka disease the spots appear on the host leaves when the plants are one or two months old. Gradually necrotic lesions appear on the stem as well. The spots on the leaves are numerous and weaken the host plant and lead to defoliation which adversely affects the size and quality of the fruits. The latter remains small in size and fewer in number.

Asexual reproduction   It takes place by the formation of long, cylindrical usually hyaline, multi-septate conidia. Some of the hyphae aggregate in the stomatal cavity and form a stroma. Conidiophores arise in tufts from the stroma and emerge through the stromata or ruptured epidermis. Conidiophores are hyaline to dark brown septate or non-septate, sometimes branched, straight or flexuous and show distinct geniculate (kneelike) bends. These form single conidia acrogenously. The mature conidia are pushed aside due to sub-apical growth of the conidiophore. This results in geniculations bearing scars of detached conidia (Figure 20.1).

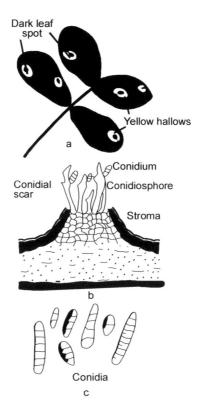

Figure 20.1 (a–c)—*Cercospora* sp. a—Leaf spots on the leaflets of *Arachis hypogea*; b—L.S. acervulus with the geniculate conidiophores emerging; c—conidia

Control measures Rotation of crops, seed treatment and disposal of infected host debris by burning or burying in deep pits eliminate chances of primary inflection from the soil-borne inoculums. The seeds within the shell are disinfected with sulphuric acid. Without shells they are soaked for half an hour in 0.5% copper sulphate solution. Agrosan GN dressing of naked seeds is equally effective.

To check secondary spread of disease, bordeaux mixture can be sprayed in the infected field. Early maturing varieties are reported to possess resistance to the discase.

Genus—*Fusarium*

Fusarium includes many species and several forms within species. Many of these are saprobic or saprophytic. Some are mild facultative parasites. Other species are parasites. All, however, have a saprophytic stage. Some of the parasitic species are soil inhabitants and can live indefinitely as soil saprophytes but some are soil invaders. The latter soon die if they are not able to infect a suitable host plant. The parasitic species cause rot of stored fruits, vegetables and are responsible for soft rot in rhizomes of ginger during storge. Some are mild root parasites and some are primarily cortical invaders which cause stem cankers and foot rot. The common species are as follows:

1. *Fusarium udum* causes wilt of *Cajanus cajan*.
2. *F. lycopersici* causes wilt of tomatoes.
3. *F. lini* causes wilt of flax.
4. *F. vasinfectum* causes wilt of cotton.
5. *F. cubense* causes the wilt of banana.
6. *F. orthaceras* causes wilt of gram.

All these species are vascular parasites and are referred to as **vascular fusaria**.

Symptoms of wilt   The susceptible plants are attached when young. The first symptom is the premature yellowing of the leaves. The next symptom is the wilting or withering of the leaves of the diseased plants. The leaves appear to be affected progressively from the bottom towards the top. Sudden wilting is rare. Finally the entire plant completely dries up.

The wilting is brought about by the plugging of the vascular tissues of the stem and roots of the host plant by dense masses of mycelial hyphae. The free flow of water to the leaves is thus interfered with. This results in drooping and wilting of the leaves of the host plants. The fungal hyphae produce toxic substances which kill the plant cells concerned in the ascent of sap. If plugging of the vascular tissue of the host takes place on one side only, the wilting is partial.

Mycelium   The mycelium is formed of septate and branched hyphae. They are both intercellular and intracellular. When young they may be colourless and become dark coloured at maturity. The dark mycelium produces thick bands which plug the vascular tissues.

Asexual reproduction   It takes place by the formation of three kinds of asexual spores. microconidia, macroconidia and chlamydospores. Sclerotia are also formed (Figure 20.2).

Microconidia   They are very small conidia abstricted from the tips of simple or branched conidiophores. The conidiophores are distinguishable from the vegetative hyphae. The conidia are oval or rounded in shape and are often held in small masses. At times they are elongated or crescent-shaped.

Macroconidia   They are large multicellular, two- to four-celled conidia. They are elongated, sickle-shaped or crescent-shaped and are produced at the tips of simple or sparingly branched conidiophores which are assembled to form sporodochium-type fructifications. These are produced in large numbers and are distributed by wind. On falling in a suitable substratum they germinate and initiate new infections.

Chlamydospores   These are rounded, oval, thick-walled cells formed in the hyphae. They may be formed singly or in chains of two or more. They become separated from the hyphae after maturity and function as resting spores. Under suitable conditions the chlamydospores germinate by germ tubes to form a fresh mycelium.

Sclerotia   The mycelium often forms compact, resting bodies of thick-walled hyphae. These are called the sclerotia. They function as storage organs and serve as a means of propagation and vegetative reproduction.

Inflection takes place through the fibrous root system near the root tip region or through wounds. The parasite then invades the root cortex and finally establishes itself in the xylem vessels. The vascular fusaria are favoured by relatively high soil temperature.

Control measures   The best method to control this disease is to produce disease-resistant varieties. Crop rotation, field sanitation and hot weather cultivation are some of the methods to eliminate soil borne infection. Antibiotics and chemicals can be used to control the disease. An antibiotic bulbuformin inhibits the growth of the pathogen.

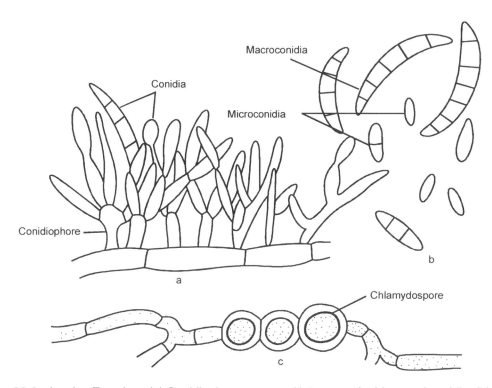

Figure 20.2   (a–c)—*Fusarium*. (a) Conidiophores grouped into sporodochium and conidia. (b) Macro and microconidia, (c) Old hyphae with intercalary chlamydospores

Genus—*Colletotrichum*

The genus belongs to the class Coelomycetes. Several species of *Colletotrichum* are parasitic on plants, causing diseases of leaves, young twigs, fruits and vegetables. The common plant pathogens are as follows:

C. falcatum on sugarcane; *C. lagenarium* on cucurbits; *C. graminicola* on seeds of cereals and grasses; *C. lindemuthianum*, anthracnose of phaseolus beans, *C. gossipi* on cotton.

Colletotrichum falcatum causes the disease red rot of sugarcane. It is a serious and destructive disease of sugarcane. It occurs in tropical and subtropical regions of the world where sugarcane is cultivated extensively.

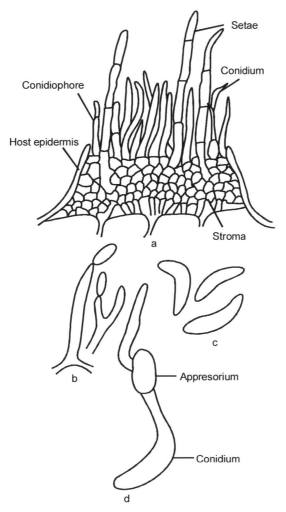

Figure 20.3 (a–d). *Colletotrichum*. (a)—Vertical section of acervulus; (b)—Conidiophores; (c)—Conidia; (d)—Germinated conidium (b–c after Buller)

Symptoms The symptoms of the disease become apparent after the rainy season on the stem and leaves. The earliest symptoms are the yellowing and drooping of the upper leaves (near the tip). In the later stages the stem shrivels, the rind looses its bright colour, become dull in appearance and longitudinally wrinkled. If the diseased stems are split open lengthwise the white pith is found reddened with patches of white running transversely across. At the advanced stage of inflection blood red lesions with dark margins develop on the midribs of the host leaves. When the acervuli are formed, these lesions become covered with powdery masses of conidia which serve to spread the disease. The disease causes enormous losses. Due to enzymatic action of the pathogen, there is conversion of sucrose in the cane juice into glucose and alcohol. Consequently there is reduction in the recoverable sugar in the factory.

Mycelium The fungus mycelium is found within and in the intercellular spaces between the pith cells of the host. The hyphae thus are both intercellular and intracellular. They are slender, colourless, branched and septate. The hyphae are hyaline in the beginning and turn dark at maturity. Cell contents also become denser and walls are thicker with the age of hyphae.

Asexual reproduction   It occurs by means of conidia. The fruiting bodies are called acervuli. In the host, the mycelial cells begin to collect beneath the epidermis to form stromata consisting of densely packed cells. From the upper surface of each stroma arise the conidiophores and bristles called setae. The setae are rigid, long hairlike structures measuring 100–200 μ long and 4 μ broad. They are septate, each with 4 septa. They either form a ring around the stroma or are intermingled with the conidiophores in the acervulus. The acervulus is saucer-shaped. The conidiophores form a closely packed palisade-like layer of phialides. The phialidic conidiophores are very small producing phialoconidia at their tips. The conidia are aseptate, fusoid, curved or sickle-shaped. They are often hyaline or slightly pink-coloured with rounded cells. They accumulate under moist conditions as glistering masses held in place by the setae. As the setae grow and push their way up, the overlying epidermis ruptures and exposes the conidia borne on small conidiophores. The conidia are readily detached and dispersed by air currents, rain, rain drop splashes and insects. They are short lived and thus germinate immediately in the presence of moisture. The conidia germinate by producing 1 to 4 (generally 2) germ tubes to give rise to new mycelium. Sometimes it produces an appresorium on coming in contact with a hard surface. The appresorium is a thick-walled structure which functions like a chlamydospore (Figure 20.3).

Control measures   Field sanitation is an important measure to prevent the build up of source of primary inoculum. It consists in the collection and burning of sugar cane trash in the field. Sound and healthy seed sets can also be used. Long rotation of crops minimizes soil-borne infection. The use of resistant varieties is the most effective of controlling the disease.

INDEX

A

Acervulus   191
Acrasiomycetes   59, 60
Aecia and aeciospores   162
Agaricales   167
Agaricus   169, 170
Agaricus (Psalliota)   167
Agaricus campestris   168, 171
Akaryotic stage   64
Albugo   18, 90
Albugo candida 92, 93, 94
Alcohol   51
Allomyces   73, 78
Allomyces arbusculus   75
Allomyces neomoniliformis   77
Ambrosia Fungi   6
Anastomosis   30
Antheridiol   28
Aphyllophorales   175
Aplanospores   18
Aquatic Fungi   2
Arthrospores   16
Ascocarp   36, 111, 131
Ascomycetes   37, 108, 110
Ascomycotina   48, 107, 112
Ascospore formation   118
Ascospores   111
Ascostroma   38
Ascus   109, 111
Aseptate mycelium 6
Asexual cycle   45
Asexual reproduction   92

Aspergillus   18, 127
Autogamy   23

B

Basidia   152
Basidia and basidiospores   161
Basidiocarp   169, 177
Basidiocarps   39, 151
Basidiomycete septum   150
Basidiomycotina   49, 147, 156
Basidiospores   151
Bipolar heterothallism   32
Blastocladiales   73
Blastomycetes   193
Budding   15

C

Candida   193
Cellulolytic Fungi   4
Cercospora   197
Chiastobasidium   154
Chlamydospores   16, 99, 199
Chytridiales   68
Chytridiomycetes   67
Cleistothecium   36, 136
Colletotrichum   200
Conidia   18
Conidiospores   18
Coprophilous Fungi   3
Cyathus   186, 187
Cyathus striatus   188
Cystogenes   76

Printed in Great Britain
by Amazon